The BUILD IT Guide to Managing the Build of your own Timber Frame Home

The BUILD IT Guide to Managing the Build of your own Timber Frame Home

ROSALIND RENSHAW

JM Dent, London

Design: Heinzight
DTP: Lemon
Illustrations: Jane Parker
Cartoons: Penelope Eaton

Made and printed in
Great Britain by
JM Dent Ltd
The Orion Publishing Group
Orion House
5 Upper St Martins Lane
London WC2H 9EA

A catalogue record for this
book is available from the
British Library

ISBN 0 460 861840

Foreword

Timber frame is the method of construction responsible for some of the oldest and most beautiful homes in Britain. It dipped out of fashion in this country, helped on its way by adverse publicity in the early eighties, when brick and block construction became increasingly widespread.

However, elsewhere timber frame has remained the most prevalent way to build houses, particularly in Scandinavia and the United States. In Scotland timber frame has always been popular. It now accounts for half of all new homes built, and eighty per cent of all new homes built privately by self builders. Will the rest of the UK catch up? Certainly, timber frame is now being seized with enthusiasm by self builders everywhere.

This is not surprising. Modern timber frame systems are literally tailor-made for anyone wanting to build, or have built, a home that is highly engineered, warmly insulated, and speedily erected. When *Build It* magazine was set up three years ago, to serve the burgeoning self build market, it rapidly became apparent that people had a great curiosity and an enthusiasm about timber frame homes.

Although the magazine simply favours self build in general rather than any particular method of construction, we soon saw the need for a really positive and comprehensive book on the subject: one that would answer people's questions, guide them through the whole process of managing the build of a timber frame home, and most of all inspire them.

This book has required considerable research, and could not have been written without the help and expertise of those in the industry. I sincerely thank everyone for their time and patience. Thanks also to those self builders who have allowed me to feature their stories and show how it's done. Particular thanks go to British Gas for their kind support for this book.

There are currently about 23,000 self builders a year in Britain, yet the very term still attracts some confusion. Self build is not necessarily about DIY but it is always about self expression. Most self builders are managers, not site labourers. They may never pick up a brick; but most will, with varying degrees of professional help, organise the build themselves. In doing so, they will reap considerable financial savings and an incredible sense of personal achievement. This book is for them, and for anyone else who might want to have a go at it one day.

Rosalind Renshaw
Editor, Build It *magazine*
Kingston-Upon-Thames
1993

The author.

Contents

Part 1: Planning

Part 1
Planning

The key to a successful, cost-effective self build is all in the planning. Aim to spend at least as long in learning about timber frame and self build, as you will spend in the actual construction. The time will not be wasted. This learning and pre-planning stage is vital.

Introduction: What is timber frame?

A timber frame house is one in which the structural strength is provided by an inner frame of timber, as opposed to an inner structure of bricks, blocks or some other masonry material.

Timber framed houses have been successfully built in Britain for centuries. They have been around since the earliest recorded times, and you can still see many of these original examples today. Tudor houses made with oak frames and exposed beams are to be found in many towns and villages. Nor are they mere museum pieces; they continue to be strong, comfortable homes, full of appeal and character, lived in by real people.

As a method of building, timber frame has proved its worth over and over again. People should remember this. Sadly, what they may remember is what has been called 'one of the most distressing episodes' in the history of building.

In 1991 an article in *Chartered Surveyor Weekly* delved into what it called *"the attempt to discredit timber frame housing."*

It went on: *"The campaign, carried out in the late 1970s, saw some involvement from the manufacturers of concrete blocks who feared a loss of business in the face of the growing popularity of timber framing. But what might have been harmless enough as a simple trade war acquired a political dimension and sprang to national prominence via television."*

The leading exponent of timber frame at that time was Sir Lawrie Barratt, whose company was the largest builder in the country. *"Sir Lawrie was also a strong supporter of Margaret Thatcher. His helicopter, which he lent to her during a general election campaign, made him a target to be shot down."*

Against this background came a television programme that was to the timber frame industry what Edwina Currie's statements about salmonella in eggs were to the poultry industry.

World in Action went out on June 27, 1983. It featured an interview with Sir Lawrie Barratt, who was apparently unaware of the programme's intentions, and whose comments were edited in juxtaposition with film of poor workmanship and site management (although it turned out that the film had not even been taken on a Barratt site).

The programme was devastating.

Until that fateful night, timber frame housing took up 23 per cent of the market. Almost overnight, as a result of the programme's suggestions that a timber frame home was a fire risk and prone to something called interstitial condensation, its market share dropped to three per cent. Millions of pounds were wiped off Barratt's shares.

Confidence faltered further as others took up the story, notably the *Sunday Times* Insight team and even the *Sun*, which abandoned its normal preoccupations.

People already living in timber frame homes paid the price. They found their homes effectively blighted. And although claims made in the programme were hotly disputed, the response by the timber frame industry was barely heard. The industry was not well-organised, it was caught on the hop, and when the various factions got together, it was to discover that their entire public relations 'fighting fund' amounted to just £8,000.

What the timber frame industry did with its budget was to think positively. It set up a centralised public relations operation and re-branded timber frame as 'timber and brick'. It is a term commonly used by manufacturers, although it can sometimes be confusing. Timber frame – as this book will show – does not, after all, have to be clad in brick; and anyway, the simple fact is, timber frame is timber frame.

Today, timber frame housing occupies around 12 per cent of the market. It is an astonishing revival, which is certain to continue from strength to strength with the publication of a report by the Building Research Establishment in the spring of 1993 which finally, and completely, vindicated timber frame as a method of construction. Even so, the industry still has some way to go, and even after ten years, those myths and misconceptions which were implanted in the public mind linger on.

But forget those recent events. Instead, visit the 16th-century Stokesay Castle Gatehouse in Shropshire, or Ann Hathaway's cottage at Stratford-upon-Avon, and marvel at the work of the craftsmen and carpenters there.

The good news is that this very same quality is available to self builders today. Indeed, some timber frame manufacturers today are still using exactly the same form of traditional oak timber frame, known as post and beam, or post and truss. The system is just as it always was, although it is now enhanced by modern standards of insulation.

Most manufacturers, however, use a system of upright 'goalposts' with rigid walling panels between, all locked together to form an immensely strong structure. This platform frame – so called, because as one floor is completed, it acts as the platform for the construction of the next – is the standard type of timber frame commonly of interest to most self builders and which most – though by no means all – of this book is about.

It is sometimes darkly hinted that this newer type of timber frame is not the same as (and must therefore be inferior to) the old type. Not true! The basic principles of both types of timber frame are exactly the same, relying on timber uprights and beams for the overall strength of the structure itself.

Arguments rage as to whether timber frame or masonry is Britain's truly 'traditional' building method. The answer is simple: both are. You will also often hear brick and block (in which the inner layer of a house wall is built of block, and the outer wall of brick) specifically described as 'traditional'. This really is a misnomer. Traditional masonry construction did not use concrete blocks at all, because they hadn't been invented! Instead, it used stone, flint and brick, and no one would dispute the fact that there are plenty of old, traditional buildings – several ancient castles, for instance – still standing, made of these materials.

Breeze blocks first appeared between the two world wars. They were usually made from a mixture of coke and furnace clinker, bound together with cement. After the last war, concrete blocks were developed, made from cement, sand and aggregate. Today's lightweight building block dates from the 1970s. There is nothing traditional about it! And that is why you will not see many old houses built of brick and ancient blockwork dotting the countryside.

Today's timber frame homes are a direct, recognisable, and high-tech descendant of those that our forebears laboured over in centuries gone by. Timber frame results in good, strong, entirely normal looking houses. Yet it is curious how little understood timber frame construction is, even by the experts, who are often sceptical about the strength and durability of the methods.

One wrote: *"There are a lot more timber-frame houses about than you might imagine – they are disguised to look like traditional houses."*

So what on earth is this terrible 'deception' which is being perpetrated on the public? Truly, there isn't one. Timber frame houses usually have a brick cladding, just as block houses do. In other words, timber frame homes can and do look just as 'normal' and just as 'traditional' as any other.

In fact the adjective 'traditional' has now become so misleading that it should no longer be used. The terms brick and block, and timber frame, are all we need.

There are basically three different types of timber frame which you will find referred to in this book.

1. Platform frame, also known as standard wall panel construction. This is the most usual type of timber frame construction and it is fully described later on. Any mention in this book of timber frame is usually a reference to this method, which has been around for at least 150 years.

2. Post and beam, also known as post and truss. This method is the oldest form of timber frame. The frame is a 'skeleton' of load-bearing upright posts and horizontal beams. The gaps in between are filled with lightweight timber panels, usually leaving the structural timbers exposed.

3. Solid timber houses (log cabins). These are usually made of interlocking, timber members which require neither external cladding nor internal decoration.

Purists might not regard these houses as true timber frame and they are probably quite right! However, let's not argue. There have been some interesting developments in this field, there is a lot of interest in them and, if I were to stick my neck out, I would predict that American styling is set to have a huge influence on house design in this country.

For the sake of completeness, there should be mention of a fourth type of timber frame (though this is the only place you will see a reference to it in the whole book). Technically known as volumetric construction, these are literally instant houses. A crane lifts pre-fabricated box units into place,

The first diagram shows the standard method of timber frame construction. This is the wall panel construction method, technically known as platform frame.

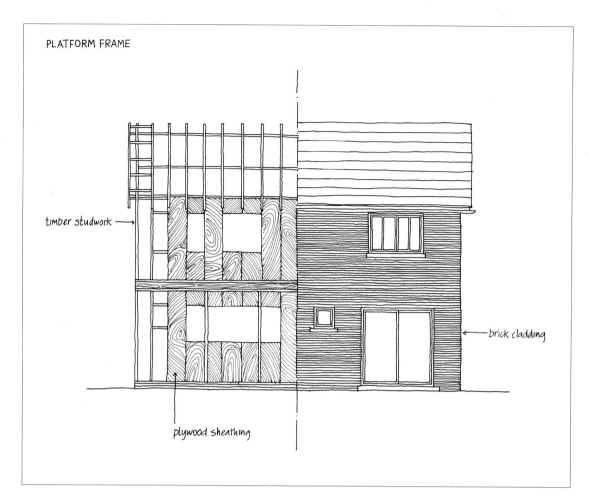

PLATFORM FRAME

timber studwork →

← brick cladding

plywood sheathing

The post and beam system is the second type of timber frame. It uses a skeletal frame which is reassuringly strong and stout and employs traditional construction methods. This is the system favoured by Border Oak.

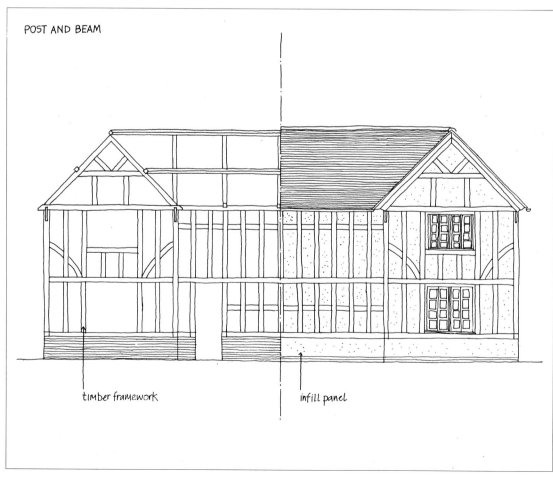

POST AND BEAM

timber framework

infill panel

SOLID TIMBER

The third type of timber frame is the solid timber or 'log' house which is based on interlocking timber walls which require neither external cladding nor internal decoration.

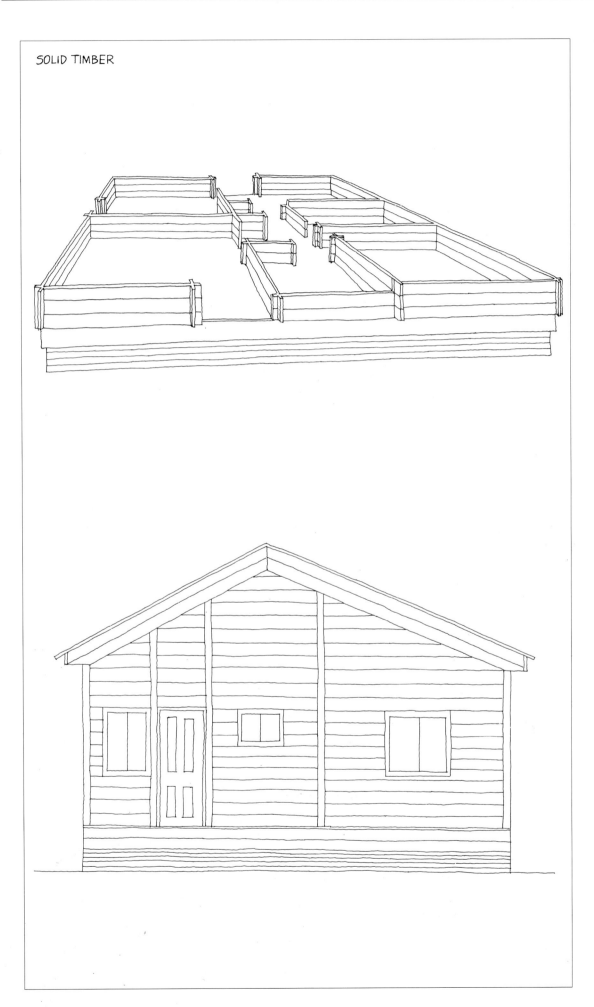

SOLID TIMBER

complete with services and decoration, to form finished houses.

What is a timber frame?

No matter how it is constructed, timber frame is, first and foremost, the result of much thought and precision. A highly engineered product, a timber frame is pre-fabricated so that all its components fit together exactly and so that the overall structure has an enormous strength which is greater than the sum of its parts.

In America (where most houses are timber frame) it is traditional for craftsmen to make each frame on site. The first thing they do on arrival is set up a dry temporary workshop where the timber can be stored and the frame made. In this country, the American specialist Roger Titus still works just like this and towards the end of this book, there is a case study where a carpenter also made his own frame on site. But generally, a timber frame is the product of computer-aided design, factory made off-site, which arrives on lorries in exactly the right quantities and which has been made so accurately that it only needs putting together.

There has been at least one timber frame home, designed by an English architect, manufactured in Scandinavia, shipped back to England, and assembled without the carpenters having to make a single cut, such is the accuracy of the method.

Like stockings and tights, the main difference between timber frame and brick and block is not their external appearance, but what holds them up.

Put simply, a timber frame house has an inner timber framework as its structural support; brick and block construction has an inner structure of blocks.

Neither framework can be seen after construction has finished, and you would not be able to tell simply by looking at a house how it had been built.

Whether the inner leaf is of timber or of blockwork, the outer leaf (or cladding) of the house is usually of brick, sometimes of stone, and occasionally of another material. In a brick and block house, the outer brick wall has some structural significance; in a timber frame house, it has none. It's there to protect the inner timber frame, and for aesthetic effect.

Not a balloon!

The method most often used in Britain today is technically known as platform frame, to distinguish it from balloon frame.

Balloon frame is barely used and involves building with wall frames which are two storeys high. Platform frame means that each storey is framed separately, each floor becoming the erection platform for the next storey.

Strength of timber frame

It is obvious to most people where the strength and solidity of a brick and block house comes from. A timber frame is lightweight, but it is also a reassuringly and enormously strong structure – in fact critics of today's building blocks often argue that timber frame is the stronger method.

Today, we are seeing a resurgence of the popularity of timber frame for houses, particularly with self builders.

This is partly because timber frame technology lends itself brilliantly to kits. Timber frames, each made to a customer's individual specification, are delivered on site and usually erected for the client. Timber frame kit houses are ideal for self builders, because they allow so much flexibility and are a quick and attractively simple way of building. This book hopes to make it simpler!

Build It magazine has been able to measure the growth of interest in timber frame for self build. When the magazine was launched in 1989, conventional wisdom was that approximately 90 per cent of all self built homes were architect designed and of brick and block construction. From the first issue, readers repeatedly showed enthusiasm for timber frame – an enthusiasm that has of necessity been reflected in our pages, though there have been accusations of bias. In late 1992, we conducted extensive research and found that amongst readers seriously contemplating self build, for every four readers wanting to know about brick and block, six wanted to learn about timber frame.

History of timber frame

Although sometimes nervously perceived by self builders as an untried and untrusted method, timber frame construction is hardly new as we have seen. It has been around for centuries, first using native oaks and then using softwood timber.

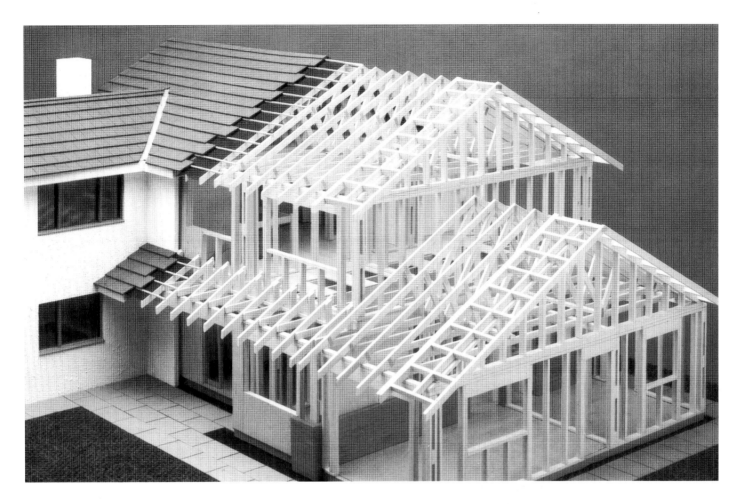

This cross-section through a timber frame house demonstrates how the basic frame is clad with brick. The tiling is also being put into place.

The use of hardwood for timber frame building began to decline throughout the 17th century, when the great oak woods of southern England were felled and not replaced. Softwood took over, especially near east coast seaside resorts, where imported fir and spruce arrived.

Softwood timber frame houses using the wall panel system have increased in popularity since the 19th century. Thousands of early examples, in Kent, Essex and Sussex, are now 150 years old and still standing today.

In the post-war building boom in this country, timber framed homes have been built in both public and private sectors. Some of the biggest residential developers (Wimpey and Barratt, for instance) have built timber frame, mainly because of its greater, and therefore more cost-effective, speed of erection. Since 1965, it's estimated that more than 700,000 timber framed houses have been built. Of the 200,000 completed under the National House-Building Council's warranty scheme, insurance claims for timber frame defects have involved only 45 houses.

But building, like every other activity of human life, is fraught with politics.

In the early eighties, a quarter of all new houses were being built with timber frame; then the industry was dealt the savage blow that brought it to its knees, reducing the number of timber frame houses to just three per cent.

This debacle served to demonstrate the power of television. One particular programme, as we have already seen at the start of this chapter, looked at timber frame, found an iffy example and drew conclusions about the whole industry which were hardly a public relations triumph. Overnight, confidence dropped like a stone, as the timber frame industry sought to shake off the criticisms – many of which, experts said at the time, were unfair.

The timber frame industry has not so much had to pick itself up off the floor as to re-invent itself (in fact, one of the first things it did after the television programme was to re-brand itself Timber and Brick). Yet rehabilitation is on its way and for several reasons.

First, timber frame has tremendous potential for social housing, as the architect Walter Segal discovered in 1962 when he needed accommodation for his family in a hurry, and built a low-cost four bedroomed timber frame bungalow in a fortnight.

The house in the picture is timber frame - but could you tell just by looking at it?

Contemporary brick and block houses are frequently not easily distinguishable from timber frame homes. The exposed external beams here are an interesting feature.

Today, the Walter Segal Self Build Trust, a non profit making charity, exists to offer information, advice, support and training to people, especially those in housing need and on low incomes, to enable them to build decent homes for themselves and their families.

Segal techniques are a simplified form of timber frame. Enterprising local authorities and housing associations in Britain are now encouraging group self build projects which utilise Segal – and take people off housing waiting lists.

Secondly, timber frame technology has made conscious and continuing efforts to improve by leaps and bounds. Never again does it want to risk unfavourable exposure, however unfair it may have been in the first place.

Thirdly, in the energy-conscious, environmentally friendly nineties, timber frame construction is seen to have attractive advantages – advantages that self builders have been quick to spot and which we'll be looking at in more detail in the next chapter.

The leaflet of the Walter Segal Self Build Trust, a charity which believes that timber frame self build can solve Britain's housing crisis.

ANYONE CAN BUILD THEMSELVES A HOME

Are you aware of the possibilities?

> ### Debate over method of construction
>
> The debate of brick and block versus timber frame seems set to continue. An article in the *Independent on Sunday* (April 26, 1992) favoured a switch to timber framed houses *"which are much better at preserving heat: built-in insulation can be of a much higher standard with timber frame inner walls than with concrete blocks.*
> *"But timber frame is being held back in England and Wales mainly for commercial reasons, such as the large stockpiles of cheap building blocks."*
> And the *Daily Telegraph* concluded: *"Condemning the whole industry is like abandoning cars because some makes were once shown to contain design faults. Since the early 1980s, it has been an article of faith among many estate agents that [timber frame] houses are unpopular and difficult to sell in damp, woodrot prone Britain, being more suitable to drier climates. That happens to be nonsense. It is worth remembering that timber framing was the principal domestic building method in many parts of the country in the 16th, 17th and even 18th centuries."*

A universal method

It's worth casting one's eyes abroad. Worldwide, some two million new timber frame homes are built each year, making it the world's most widely used building method. In other western countries, around 70 per cent of all new low-rise family houses and bungalows are timber frame. Blocks never did catch on in Scandinavia, Canada or the USA.

The future of self build and timber frame

The individual self build market is growing. It continued to grow even during the recession of the late 1980s and early nineties. By 1991, the number of new houses built by developers had dropped by six per cent; yet the number of new self built homes that year rose by four per cent, to an estimated 23,000.

Given the increasing enthusiasm for timber frame among the growing ranks of self builders, and the number of timber frame specialists which have sprung up to serve the market, it stands to reason that timber frame will be the most popular choice of construction for more people.

Social self build is also on the increase, and the whole key to it is timber frame. Individual self build - the subject of this book - and social self build are two quite different activities. But there are common bonds. First, the interest in, and widespread acceptance of, timber frame; and secondly, self builders of all types have a spirit of get-up-and-go. They are not prepared to wait for someone else to provide them with a house. It is something they want to achieve for themselves – and can do easily with timber frame.

There will always be folk who settle for mass-built, mass-marketed homes put up on giant estates by mass-developers, even though they will complain that the only way they can express their individuality is in the choice of bathroom tiles. But increasingly, the pattern of housing in Britain will move closer to the American mixture of self build and homes specifically built to order. Virtually every home in the States is timber frame.

The appeal of timber frame in this country is surely set to grow. For self builders, it is a method of building that people who are largely amateurs, can both understand and control with relative ease, and which offers an end product that is highly individual, energy efficient, and environmentally friendly.

Timber frame is not a method which has had its day, but one whose time has finally come. Why is this? Because it is:

- **Speedy**

- **Substantial**

- **Energy efficient**

- **Environmentally friendly**

- **Flexible in design**

- **Fully recognised by financial institutions and building societies, and by the NHBC (National House Building Council)**

- **Ideal for self build**

Some of these points we have already touched on; all will be examined in detail in the chapters to come.

Chapter 1: Timber frame – the benefits

Enthusiasts need no convincing of the benefits of timber frame. In fact, they think there is no other way to build! Sceptics prefer to argue. Either way, the various claims bear further scrutiny.

Cost-effective method

Timber frame construction is often claimed to be cost-effective. Let's be cautious about this. Cost-effective does not necessarily mean cheap, and a great deal depends on how each individual house is actually executed.

In theory, and usually in practice, a timber frame house is both economical to build and economical to run. However, it should be pointed out that prices of timber frames vary enormously from supplier to supplier. A 100 per cent variation in price is not uncommon, which is staggering by any standards.

Shop until you drop!

The first and overriding message has to be: shop around. Never, ever go to just one timber frame supplier. Compare as many prices and packages as you can.

Don't allow yourself to be clouded by assumptions. In particular, never assume that a famous company with a huge turnover, is going to be cheaper than a small little-known firm, or vice versa; never assume that a company hundreds of miles away is bound to cost more than one on your doorstep (you may be in for a pleasant surprise!); don't assume that all the timber frame specialists belong to a trade body of some kind - a proportion do, but many first-rate companies don't.

Most importantly, never assume that comparisons are straightforward - they aren't, because the packages themselves vary so much. Go to as many companies as you possibly can, look at their prices, specifications and services, and explore all possibilities – shopping around can save you literally thousands of pounds. And don't stop at suppliers: as this book will show later on, there is nothing to prevent you putting together your own package, using your own architect, finding a co-operative manufacturer (and most are), and even employing your own erection team.

Low labour costs

In comparison with timber frame, blocks seem very cheap to buy. But there are two 'buts'.

First, it is impossible to make direct comparisons. A block is, after all, a block. A timber frame is much more than a wall, and will normally also include some or all of the following: roof trusses, floor joists, internal partitions, erection labour, insulation, windows, doors, staircase, plasterboard, glazing, skirtings and architraves (the ornamental band around a door or window).

The second 'but' is that, although blocks are a comparatively inexpensive material, they require that labour should be on site for a relatively long time. And labour, as everyone knows, is expensive.

This is where timber frame scores, because it has a head start over brick and block construction due to the sheer speed of erection. Thus labour costs are low, and the speed is good for the cash flow.

Stay dry

Because a timber frame house is so quickly weathertight, it means that the inside of the house is dry, safeguarding your investment in materials such as trusses and joists.

No 'wet' trades, such as plastering which needs gallons of water, are used inside a timber frame house, and this too has a beneficial cost effect. It means not having to wait for mortar and plaster to dry out, which in turn means you can move into a timber frame house much more quickly. If you are paying extra interest charges during the build (as you may well be) then this will save you money. Being able to move quickly could also mean a saving on rent, since many self builders will be renting while the build is in progress.

Site security

In terms of site security and insurances during the build, it is also clearly cheaper to be able to complete the build quickly. And finally, because of the overall speed of construction, the self builder will be able to finish the build and reclaim VAT that much sooner. That, too, is good for cash flow.

Performance of timber frame

So much for the construction; now for the

performance. How cost-effective is a timber frame home? This is where the arguments really hot up!

Timber frame houses have a very quick thermal response. In other words, they heat up very quickly, which suits most modern lifestyles particularly well. As a method, timber frame construction lends itself to outstanding thermal performance – not merely meeting the thermal insulation requirements of Building Regulations, but actually improving on them by at least 25 per cent. Many self builders use enhanced insulation to improve on this further.

This is because part and parcel of the construction is the use of non-combustible insulating material packed into the frame. Together with the roof insulation and double glazing which the majority of self builders routinely fit, it means that the building is cheaper and easier to heat.

Brick and block houses can and do also achieve very high standards of warmth and insulation, but not as standard. Indeed, most self builders, using either method, would – even should – be very keen to achieve a good score under the new National Homes Energy Rating scheme. The first three houses to achieve perfect (ten out of ten) scores under the NHER were all timber frame.

Easily extended

There is a common perception that while it's easy to pop an annexe on to a brick and block built house, it's virtually impossible to extend a timber frame home. It is extremely hard to know where this myth came from, or why it is perpetuated, but it certainly isn't true.

Because of its modular construction, timber frame homes can be very easily extended – so easily, in fact, that this counts as a definite plus point. Whether the timber frame itself is the standard panelled kind, or of post and beam, it will lend itself easily and quickly to extension.

To extend, no great demolition work is needed, and the structural integrity of the timber frame is not affected – well, not unless you do something really daft, like dismantle a load-bearing upright. Nor will there be clouds of dust because of the need to take down internal blockwork. To extend a timber frame house is primarily a matter of removing the outer cladding where you want to extend, taking down panels and adding on another module or bay.

Similarly, a timber frame house is easy to alter. This is particularly relevant at the planning stage where one of the great pleasures of looking at designs is the ability to move partitions, swap rooms from left to right or vice versa (known as handing), drop in extra windows and doors, and even create extra rooms. I should know – my own timber frame home is proof!

Most kit house suppliers say that their houses are actually designed for alteration and growth. Potton, one of the best known names in the industry, for instance, say that both their Heritage and Rectory house ranges fit this category, and that extensions are as easy to plan as to carry out. Indeed, it's perfectly possible to start with one of the smaller house types in either range, and extend it into one of the bigger ones.

At least one kit supplier, Jones Homes, even does what it calls an 'extendable' home in its standard range. The accommodation of the Colwyn is specifically designed to be progessively increased over the years. What starts off as a three bedroomed house with a floor area of 1,039 square feet can end up with four bedrooms, an extra reception room, and a larger kitchen and hall. It is an attractive concept for a family which is likely to increase in size and spending power over the years.

Scandinavian timber frame houses are as easy to extend as any other. Gunnel Westley, Managing Director of Scandia-Hus, a leading Scandinavian house supplier, extended her own home some years after it was built, by adding on a large indoor swimming pool complex. She also has several clients who have added to their homes – though perhaps not quite as ambitiously. Her company also does a bungalow which is designed from the outset to become a chalet-style house.

The only major precaution to take when extending a timber frame house is to ensure that fire stops and cavity barriers within the external walls of the frame, are reinstated. You are, however, unlikely to forget, because the building inspector will remind you!

Speed of erection

The rate at which a timber frame goes up can be awe-inspiring. If you are managing your self build, do take the week off to enjoy the spectacle – and incidentally, to be able to put paid to a few more myths, notably that it will take four to six people to

As seen from these floor plans, Potton's Heritage range of homes can easily be extended from the compact to the luxurious. You could even start with an Arrington and extend it to an Abbotsley. (Copyright Potton 1981)

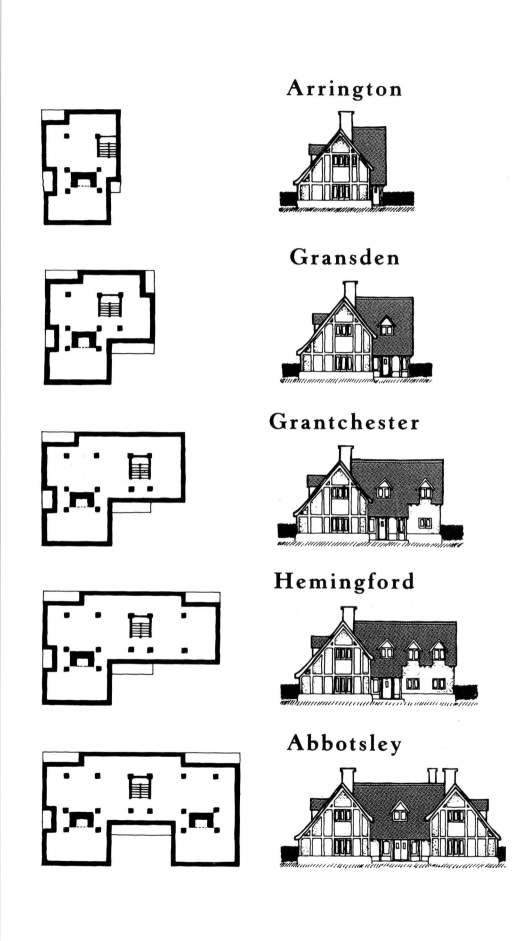

Arrington

Gransden

Grantchester

Hemingford

Abbotsley

erect your shell, and preferably also a crane. When our own 3,000 square foot timber frame house was being built, we hardly dared turn away for a second for fear of missing some of the action. A team of three started work on the Monday morning, and had finished by Friday morning, no cranes required.

In general, the shell of an average-sized timber frame house will go up inside a week. Some will go up even more quickly. It's very exciting.

A Scandinavian-style house with large walls, complete with glazed windows and pre-hung doors, may go up inside a day (and yes, that will require a crane). That's even more exciting!

A lot will depend on the experience of the team of erectors. But to see skilled joiners at work really is something – and knocks forever on the head the misconception that a timber frame is the housing equivalent of flat-pack furniture which is somehow 'thrown up'. Absolutely nothing could be further from the truth.

Once the frame is up, the whole shell can be made swiftly watertight. The roof trusses are felted and battened, in other words covered with roofing felt which is held in place by the roof battens. This makes the roof ready for tiling. To get to this stage may take a total of only eight days or less; if you were building with brick and block, it would probably take six weeks.

This is the reason why any show house at an exhibition is much more likely to be timber frame than brick and block. There usually isn't enough time available to build the latter.

Exhibition show house

The record for building a timber frame house must surely go to Medina Gimson, who supplied the show house at the 1992 National Self Build Homes Show at Alexandra Palace. It was completed in just three days – and, one should add, nights. In this timescale, the house was not only built, but tiled, bricked, decorated, fitted and equipped, and completed in every detail. This could only have been achieved by using timber frame construction, and the frame itself went up inside twelve hours!

More speed

The second speed advantage becomes evident when work starts inside the house.

A brick and block house will probably be plastered in the traditional way. This will involve an enormous amount of water being almost literally poured into the construction process – about 1,500 gallons, typically, in an average family home.

A timber framed house, however, will be dry-lined with plasterboard. It will then be ready for instant decorating. There will be no delay while the house dries out, and no fear of shrinkage cracks or damp staining.

In theory and usually in practice, a timber framed house will be built more quickly, and ready to move into much sooner. It is not unknown for people to move into their fully finished, brand new timber frame homes inside 12 weeks flat.

For most people, it makes enormous financial sense to maximise the speed possible with timber frame, and this is a matter of good management and pre-planning as we'll be seeing later in this book.

But no matter what your own time scale is, timber frame's speed still works in your favour. Your build and materials are not at the mercy of the weather for so long, and, because your house becomes watertight very quickly, it enables the rest of the work to continue comfortably and enjoyably in the dry.

Insulation and energy efficiency

Timber framed houses are wrapped in insulation, which means that they can be ultra energy efficient.

It is important to know exactly where the insulation goes, because many people might – wrongly – assume it went between the outer brick cladding, and the inner structure. Here, however, there should be a clear 50mm cavity which must always be maintained. It is there to ensure that the inner leaf is kept completely dry.

Look at the sketch on page 27, and you will see that in fact the insulation is tucked between the vapour check, which comes just before the plasterboard lining, and the sheathing board.

In post and beam timber frame, there will be a different form of insulation, with infill panels insulated with polystyrene between the oak frame. In the old days, this infill would have been wattle and daub, made up of materials like horse manure

Victoria Cottage was built by Medina Gimson at the 1992 National Self Build Homes Show in just three days flat, a convincing demonstration of the speed of timber frame erection.

FIRST FLOOR
VARIATION A 4 BEDROOM

FIRST FLOOR
VARIATION B 3 BEDROOM

FIRST FLOOR
VARIATION C 3 BEDROOM WITH GALLERY

and mud, held together with straw, twigs and horsehair which was the Elizabethans' idea of home insulation.

It was probably reasonably effective, and indeed if you are keen and like the smell, there is no reason why you shouldn't try it now, assuming that you can find an obliging horse.

With solid wood homes, the insulation is different again. Usually, there is a core of insulating material inside the timber panels.

Thermal insulation

Modern timber frame insulation ensures that in winter, the whole house is comfortably heated with no cold areas or internal condensation, and that in summer, it is cool and airy.

Thermal performance is measured in U-values, which measure how much heat energy is lost. The lower the U-value, the better.

Building Regulations have gradually brought U-values down over the years; originally, timber frame houses were built to achieve a U-value of 0.68, at a time when the mandatory requirement for all new houses was 1.70. Since 1982, the minimum insulation level for walls in England, Wales and Scotland, has been 0.6. Although this figure has been revised (in 1990 and 1991) down to 0.45, in practice the higher figure still applies. This is because the 'trade-off' provisions (complicated, but the way Building Regulations work) allow walls with a U-value of 0.6 to be retained, if double glazing is used instead of single glazing.

Timber frame houses, as standard, do 25 per cent better than even the lower 0.45 figure whereas tests have cast doubt on the true U-values of a brick and block wall, re-calculated to have a real U-value not of 0.6, but 0.9 (Eurisol report, 1991). The report says: "*A true U-value of 0.9 W/m2K means that heat losses might be 50 per cent greater than Building Regulations allow.*"

Eurisol, the Mineral Wool manufacturers trade body, estimates that since 1982, 800,000 houses have been built which did not comply with the U-values laid down in Building Regulations; these houses will probably cost an extra £2 billion to heat during their lifetime, dumping nearly 30 million tonnes of carbon dioxide into the atmosphere from electricity generation. Comparisons were made of the U-values of four walls of different construction – brick and block, with an insulated cavity earned

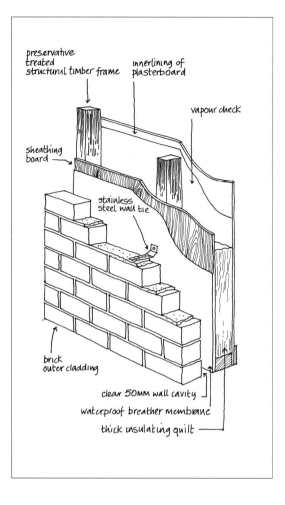

preservative treated structural timber frame

innerlining of plasterboard

vapour check

sheathing board

stainless steel wall tie

brick outer cladding

clear 50mm wall cavity
waterproof breather membrane
thick insulating quilt

The different layers that make up a timber frame house are clearly shown in this cross-section which indicates the position of the insulation between the sheathing board and the timber frame itself. Note also the cavity between the brick cladding and the frame.

0.53; brick and block, with an empty cavity, scored 0.76; the two timber stud walls scored 0.39 and 0.28 respectively, depending on the level of insulation.

A 90mm thick mineral fibre quilt tucked into the external walls of a timber frame house gives a U-value of 0.35 (Wimpey Laboratories research). It's possible to do better than this. Ecowall, for instance, a wall panel system developed by the Timber Research and Development Association (TRADA), and Raab Karcher, the parent company of Medina Gimson, achieves 0.23. The U-value of a wall of a Spaceframe house has been measured as 0.11.

But what of brick and block?

Architect Arthur Quarmby, writing in *Roofing, Cladding and Insulation*, commented that the tests quoted in the Eurisol report "*all show that the insulation of the conventional brick and foamed block cavity wall falls far short of what the manufacturers claim.*"

He described this as 'a swiz' and went on to express further worries.

"In attempting to meet increasing standards of thermal insulation, the lightweight, and especially the foamed, concrete block manufacturers have gone too far. Their products are now so weak, friable and absorbent that they are no longer capable of doing an acceptable structural job. So much we have all known for quite a long time. But we thought that at least we were getting the insulation we were paying for. Now it is evident that insulation standards were only met by unreliable means, and we are not getting half the insulation we expected."

And he concluded: *"I very much fear that the masonry wall has had it. Unless some miraculous new products are introduced we are going to have to change to some form of construction which really can delivery the insulation which we require. And that seems inevitably to point us towards timber – or at least some form of frame-construction, and an outer skin which really does turn the weather."*

Energy Rating Scheme

The Energy Rating scheme is something we will all be hearing more and more about. It assesses houses and gives them a rating to show their energy

efficiency. Soon, all new houses will have to be given an energy rating. The National Homes Energy Rating scheme takes a number of factors into account as well as insulation (for instance, the siting and orientation of the house, whether it has an open chimney, and so on).

Under the NHER houses are assessed to receive scores up to ten. Houses built to the 1990 Building Regulations score seven, as opposed to the national average of 4.4. Timber frame homes have been scoring into the high nines. Some, as we have said, have even scored the perfect ten. Certificates issued under this scheme will also produce a further measure of energy efficiency. This will be the S.A.P. or Government Standard Assessment procedure figure which will be, very roughly, ten times the NHER scale. This figure is likely in future to be accepted by the Building Control Authorities as proof of compliance with part 'L' of the regulations (conservation of Fuel and Power).

Taken to its limits, the idea of an energy efficient timber frame home that requires no central heating at all, but relies on a very thick quilt of insulation, and is heated passively (ie, by people simply living in it), is perfectly possible.

In fact, *Build It* magazine has already featured two – a Spaceframe bungalow where the owners claim never to have switched their central heating system on at all in ten years. And the remarkable three storey house of Mr Edward Akister, which was completed in 1991, and which has no central heating at all, only a heat exchange system, by which used air from warm places in the home such as the bathroom or just above the cooker, is passed over a heat exchanger. This retains something like 70 per cent of this heat, which is then mixed with incoming fresh air.

Thermal mass

You may hear the great thermal mass argument advanced from time to time. The nub of it is that brick and block has a greater thermal mass and therefore retains heat. In contrast, the lightweight structure of a timber frame house has a quick thermal response. It heats up fast, but also cools down quickly – or does it?

In fact, most new timber frame houses are so very well insulated that they not only heat up quickly, but they also retain the heat just as well, as tests (by Wimpey Laboratories) show. In terms of energy

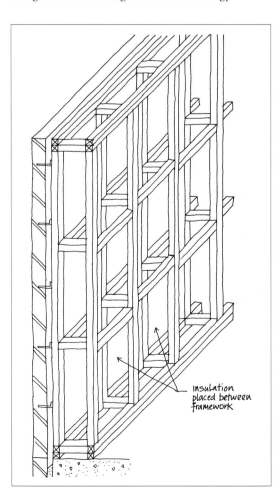

Insulation placed between framework

This variation (patented by Spaceframe) on a standard timber frame shows doubled-up walls, allowing room for more insulation and thus improving heat efficiency.

A home without central heating

Several things make the four-storey home of Edward Akister unusual. First and foremost, it is designed to be so energy efficient that it has no central heating system; secondly, it has been built on difficult ground that would make the most experienced builder feel discouraged.

Mr Akister, who lives in Ironbridge, Shropshire, nevertheless succeeded, and he believes that the result is a home for the 21st century, being almost completely 'green' in concept.

He designed the house himself, and applied for planning permission in 1987. The house has a lower ground floor of brick and concrete, topped by three timber framed floors, made by Swedhouse of Sweden. The frame has an outer plywood skin to act as permanent bracing. These plywood panels, each containing an insulated inner layer covered by internal plasterboard, were bolted on to the actual frame, using metal brackets also designed by Mr Akister.

There are eight bedrooms and five bathrooms, all with water-saving toilets.

Planning permission was achieved without difficulty; the biggest challenge was the site, which is in an area that has been heavily mined for clay, coal and limestone. This meant potential subsidence, caused by old shafts. A site survey was carried out and recommended drilling down 100 feet, to create an underground solid concrete mass which would anchor the foundations, which would themselves be reinforced with steel.

Mr Akister managed the build himself, employing sub-contractors. The house was finished in September 1991, and has attracted enormous local interest. Two 'open' days brought in many visitors, and raised £150 for charity.

There is no central heating whatever, only a Norwegian heat exchange system by Flebu Ltd. This is located in the loft, and works by extracting warm air from the living areas and mixing it with fresh incoming air. Doors, walls, and roof are all insulated, and windows triple glazed. There is also sound insulation internally, between floors and in partitions.

Building costs (labour and materials) totalled £150,000. The value of the land, already owned by Mr Akister, has since been established at £60,000. Market value today has been put at between £350,000 and £500,000.

---

efficiency, you could also try asking yourself whether you really want to live in Conway Castle, perhaps the ultimate example of thermal mass. But imagine those heating bills!

A 'green' house

No new house can be described as completely friendly to the environment. Timber frame houses can, however, justifiably claim to be friendlier than most. The friendship is partly about the level of insulation. The greater their thermal efficiency, the less energy houses use up, which means lower emissions of carbon dioxide, the 'greenhouse' gas that causes global warming. The insulation itself is also important – in any house, timber frame or otherwise, it should be free of Chlorofluorocarbons.

A timber framed home uses naturally produced materials. Wood uses around 20 per cent less energy to bring it to its finished state than other construction materials.

A masonry house typically requires about 64,000 kWh of primary energy, taking into account manufacturing, transportation and work on site. A timber frame house of the same size will require 51,000.

All timber frame used in this country comes from sustainable sources – properly managed areas where three tree seedlings are planted for every one that is harvested. Timber is usually said to be the world's most ecologically friendly material. Young growing trees absorb CO_2, converting it into oxygen. Mature trees have slower growth rates, requiring less CO_2, and producing less oxygen. Environmentally, therefore, it's a good thing to have a periodic tidy-up of older trees, and replace them with young, growing specimens.

That said, most timber frame in this country has to be imported, so there is an argument that gains in environmental-friendliness are somewhat lost by having to transport timber long distances (although the total energy figures quoted take account of this). Probably some of the most ecologically acceptable timber framed houses resulted from the great hurricane of 1987 which swept the south of Britain, and felled many oak trees.

Logically, perhaps, the most environmentally friendly houses of all are constructed on the spot, from local materials, which is why the American tradition of timber frames being made from felled trees on the site of the new home, is as 'green' as it is possible to be. However, be warned. The Scottish Consortium of Timber Frame Industries has expressed concern about the quality control, or its lack, of on-site manufacture of frames. It has also recommended that all timber frame structures should be manufactured under factory conditions. Moral: go green, but go carefully!

Finally, timber frame produces no radon gas, now thought to be implicated in cancer. As such, it has not been implicated in recent scare stories about the possible health risks of some building materials.

Various aspects of the unusual four-storey house built by Mr Akister. The site chosen was a very challenging one, demanding extensive foundations and close attention to design details.

The Akister house is full of
light and space, an effect
which is further enhanced by
the abundant use of glass
and attractive wood.

This original tile mosaic
which blends well with the
colours of the wood is
another interesting feature
of the Akister house.

Checklist

A timber frame home:

- Needs the same attention to foundations and
  groundwork as any other type of construction
- Is highly engineered
- Is quick to erect
- Does not use wet trades internally –
  so there's no waiting for walls to dry
- Has no cracks or damp stains due to plaster
  drying out
- Has a standard thermal performance that
  easily out-performs Building Regulations
- Is readily extended
- Is relatively friendly to the environment
- May be a building method unfamiliar to some
  workers in the building industry

A brick and block home:

- Needs the same attention to foundations and
  groundwork as any other type of construction
- Is not engineered in the same way, because
  its structure is not of a pre-fabricated timber
  frame, but of blocks which are laid on site
- Is slower to erect
- Does use wet trades, and it can take weeks
  for walls to dry
- There may be cracks or damp stains due
  to plaster drying out
- Has a thermal performance which should
  meet Building Regulations requirements,
  and which can be enhanced
- Is readily extended
- Is said to be less friendly to the environment
- Is a familiar form of construction to the
  building industry
- Has only 30% less timber in its construction
  than a timber frame house

Chapter 2: Problems and solutions

Timber frame homes have a reputation for being good in terms of heat insulation, but poor in terms of sound insulation. It is often suggested that a timber frame house is noisy to live in. This argument really does not have any solid factual basis.

For a start, although it is accepted that a solid block wall does indeed absorb noise efficiently, the fact is that there are very few solid block walls inside a modern house. The internal walls of virtually all new houses are of precisely the same construction, which is stud partitions covered with plasterboard.

The sound insulation inside virtually any new house, whether it is constructed of timber frame or brick and block, is therefore identical.

But even if you did have solid block walls inside your house, how much difference would it really make, given that sound travels through gaps? The noisiest houses are those with doors and windows open. In addition, actual measurements of finished homes have demonstrated that the best

sound insulation for separating or party walls is offered by timber frame. Indeed, the Building Research Establishment has concluded that if sound insulation could always be as good as that measured in party walls of timber framed terraced and semi-detached houses, the problem of noise from neighbours would be greatly reduced.

But let me be subjective for just a minute. External noise is not in my experience a problem. Personally, I find one of the great pleasures of living in a timber frame house is its tranquillity. Perhaps it's just me, but I feel that timber framed houses offer a unique sense of being cocooned. I think that external sounds simply do not penetrate. With a busy motorway in earshot once I step outside my house, this is something to be appreciated. I can honestly say that every timber framed house I have visited has exactly this quality of peace.

Sometimes, this efficient insulation against external noise can have its drawbacks, as is the case with the man who built a highly insulated timber frame

A Berghus, self built in Cornwall by Dick Tuson. It is by the sea, but so well insulated that the sound of the waves crashing on the beach below cannot be heard inside.

house by the Cornish coast, and rather to his disappointment, found he couldn't hear the sea! However, if exceptional external noise is likely to be a problem – as it was for a development of timber frame houses built under the landing path of Heathrow Airport – it is extremely easy to obtain maximum external wall acoustic performance.

All that was needed in this case was to use thicker wall studs, and greater insulation. In terms of cost, the extra wall thickness was not regarded as significant.

With any new build, it is also worth paying attention to the acoustic performance inside the house. Let's not be coy about this: will you be able to hear what your visitors do in the loo? If someone has a rampant sex life, will everyone else in the household know all about it?

If you want to create an outstandingly peaceful living environment with very good sound insulation between rooms, you can achieve it quite easily.

The first, and most vital step is simply to ensure that work is carried out to a high standard. The importance of this cannot be overstated. There really is no reason for floorboards to creak, or for plumbing pipes to clank. Pipes can now be held in place and they should also be lagged as they pass through the joists.

Secondly, you can either insulate some or all of your ceilings and internal walls by using thicker plasterboard, or better still, use double thickness of board on each face of the wall. You could also drop a quilt of insulation between the two boards. In any case make sure all perimeter gaps are tight fitting or, even better, place a bead of mastic behind the skirtings and at ceiling level.

You should at any rate insulate the walls round your loos, a requirement that NHBC builders have to fulfill. What is usually specified is either a double thickness of plasterboard, or a quilt of mineral wool inside the studwork. Upstairs, you could sound insulate bedrooms in the same way.

If you are keen to ensure a good standard of sound insulation throughout your home, discuss this before you order your timber frame, so that you can work out all the implications, including those of fitting and of cost.

Prejudice and timber frame

Ever since the television programme of 1983, there have been various myths and misconceptions to do with timber frame houses. However, fears that they run with condensation, catch fire easily, and will fall down anyway in a couple of years time, are all unfounded. Nor is it true that you must not make a single mistake during the construction process; or that you must not hammer nails in the walls.

Building societies and insurance societies are perfectly happy to deal with timber frame homes, even if you have heard to the contrary, and there is no reason whatever why a timber frame home should fail to attract buyers.

Timber frame construction is, as has already been stated, very strong and durable. There are thousands of beautiful old timber framed houses all over Britain which show that it is a method capable of lasting centuries. Although there are plenty of clever know-alls around who will tell you: *"Ah, but today's timber frame is different,"* that simply isn't the case. Today's method is a direct descendant of the historic construction process. The underlying principles are the same; the only differences are those made by advanced technology.

Timber frame is durable, and provided a timber frame house is constructed properly, there is absolutely no evidence to show that it is in danger of rot or fire. The timber frame house in *World in Action* was indeed suffering from rot, but it had been clad by virtue of rendered chicken wiring! Even so, it had successfully stood the elements for some years.

As for fire, the building process of timber frame requires several precautions. These include cavity barriers incorporated into the cavity between the timber frame and the outer cladding, to act as fire stops. All other building regulations about fire prevention must be complied with, and insurance companies will not distinguish between timber frame and masonry built houses when it comes to premiums.

According to the Building Research Establishment, timber frame houses are as safe as any other: *"In a far reaching investigation of fires in dwellings, the Fire Research Station has found no evidence that injury or death in fires are more likely to occur in timber frame dwellings than in any other form of construction."*

Noggings are short lengths
of timber fixed horizontally
between studs, on to which
all wall-hung items can
be fixed.

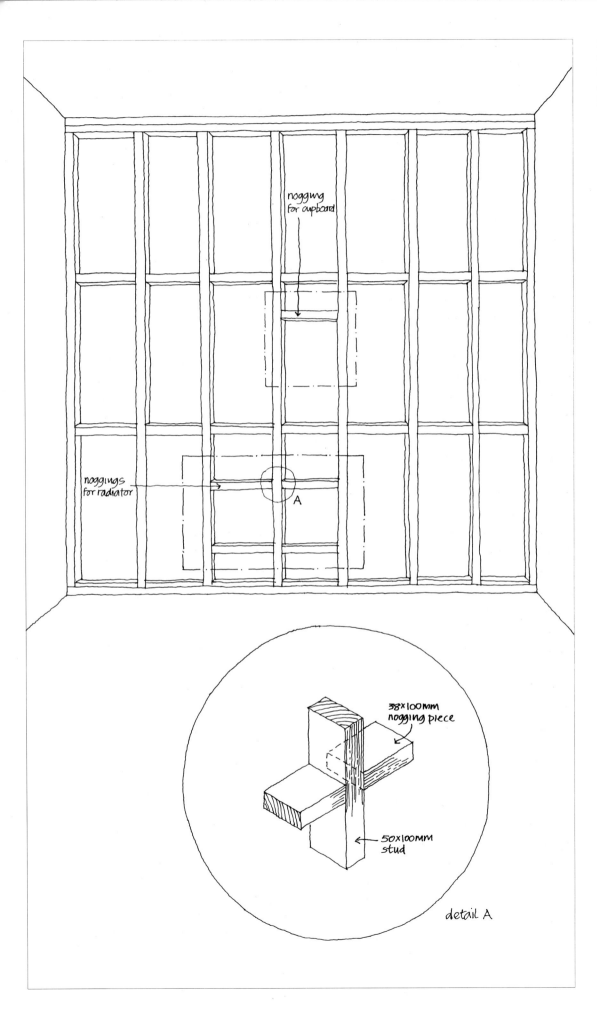

nogging
for cupboard

noggings
for radiator

A

38×100mm
nogging piece

50×100mm
stud

detail A

Nor is there any evidence of condensation damaging the timber frame structure and causing rot. Interstitial condensation is the name given to water vapour which condenses within the structure of the house.

The structure of a timber frame is, however, protected against damp in several ways:

first, by the cavity between the outer cladding and the timber frame;

secondly by the use of vapour and moisture checks;

and thirdly by treating the sole plates (the part of the structure on which the rest of the timber frame stands) and wooden panels that are the framework of the building.

If something goes wrong?

Many self builders live in fear of something going wrong during construction. They worry that the vapour barrier will be pierced, or that driving rain will penetrate the outer brick cladding to soak the inner timber frame, or that the cavity will be accidentally breached and that condensation from inside the house will rot the timber framework.

However, between 1984 and 1990 the Building Research Establishment monitored 400 houses to see whether condensation had occurred in any of them over that period. It hadn't. These houses included ones where there had been the kind of fault mentioned above – no one, of course, wants faults to occur, but as is the way of things, they occasionally do. The research showed not one instance of decay to the timber frame, even where there had been a problem during or after construction.

Noggings

One disadvantage of timber frame often cited is that, because the walls are not solid like block, you cannot simply seize a rawplug and blithely hammer it into the walls to put up a shelf whenever and wherever you feel like it. That statement does need qualifying: today, you can use thick, good quality plasterboard which is perfectly capable of holding up pictures and, with special fixings, wall-hung radiators.

With heavy objects (wash basins, for instance), you may simply screw these straight into the vertical studs.

But the best answer of all is noggings.

Noggings sounds like something that could be 100 per cent proof which you drink on a cold day. Sadly, this is not true. Do not confuse a nogging with a noggin!

A nogging is a timber batten, horizontally fixed between the vertical wooden studs, before the plasterboard is fixed, and on to which you subsequently fix all wall-hung items.

Many believe that the humble nogging is the invisible and unsung hero of timber frame construction. With noggings in place, you will be able to fix heavy kitchen cupboards, pictures, radiators, shelves, or that magnificent pair of ornamental antlers belonging to the stag that Uncle Bertie shot back in 1932.

Noggings, however, do require forward planning. As soon as the timber frame is erected, work out exactly where you are going to need noggings and for what purpose. Try to work out the requirements you know about now, as well as the ones you don't. In other words, allow for the possibility that in future, you will want to add extra wall-hung cabinets, shelves, pictures and so on. It is much, much better to over-estimate the noggings than to under-estimate them.

Many self builders like to put up their own noggings; otherwise, you could get a carpenter to spend a day doing them. Then try and remember where your noggings are!

This is obviously important, because once the plasterboard is up, you will have lost sight of them.

The well organised self builder will take pictures, do sketches, mark the noggings on some master plan or even (and it's a very good idea) take a camcorder round to note their position. The slightly less well organised will buy a little device (around £15) that specifically locates noggings. The barely organised brigade will endeavour to locate noggings by tapping on the wall, and listening out for what sound like the solid bits!

Chapter 3: Finding land

Whether you are planning to build a brick and block house, or a timber framed one, you obviously cannot be a self builder without a plot of land. There are a number of different ways in which you can set about finding one.

Estate agents

Local estate agents are becoming increasingly aware of the self build market, and either may already have plots for sale or will be willing to deal on your behalf. If the latter is the case, there may be a fee to pay, so check first to ensure that this won't be an unseen extra.

Plots are frequently sold at auction; check with local papers and estate agents for announcements. If you think you might be interested in buying at an auction sale, take legal and financial advice first because you must be in a position to proceed with your purchase immediately. In practice, this will mean that you must have sold any previous house. You will need at least a month before the auction to carry out legal searches and get your finance in place.

Power of the press!

Local newspapers frequently advertise building land for sale, so ensure you buy all local publications; you could also try advertising yourself under the land wanted section. Word your advertisement so that you make it clear that you are a private buyer, looking for a plot of a certain size, in a specific price bracket. *Exchange and Mart*, and *Build It* magazine are good sources of plots.

Local councils

You can also extend your search for a plot to local authorities and other authorities (British Rail, any of the utilities such as water authorities) who may have land to sell. Ask your solicitor or other professional advisor (eg chartered surveyor) to make an approach on your behalf; alternatively, simply write a letter of enquiry direct to the chief executive, in the case of a council, or the appropriate area manager in the case of a utility.

Developers

Development companies, from the largest right down to the smaller local builders, may also have plots which they would prefer to sell rather than to develop. One enterprising self builder built two successive homes on plots which had remained undeveloped on small building sites where the developers in question had quite simply run out of cash.

Developers quite often want to off-load building plots which they have acquired, but prefer not to advertise the fact as they do not want to be seen to be disposing of their land banks. A direct inquiry to the development company is the best approach.

Land finding companies

There are a few land finding companies who operate nationally and specialise in plot searching for individuals. These companies advertise (again, try the relevant magazines), and exhibit. Typically they charge £25 for a quarterly subscription which would give you monthly lists of plots of the type and location in which you have expressed interest. A bit like a computer dating system!

On top of the basic subscription charge, you would pay more if you wanted to use services for a feasibility study or a survey.

Some timber frame companies also have plot finding resources, though these are usually fairly localised to their own headquarters.

Self help

Self builders frequently track down land for themselves simply by driving around and looking for it. You can find out who the land belongs to by checking with the Land Registry. The Land Registry cannot find plots for you, but it can supply you with information such as the name and address of the legal owner of registered land, and it shows whether there are any restrictions on their power to sell, such as a mortgage or other financial charge on the land. There is a useful leaflet published by the Land Registry called *The Open Register – A guide to information held by the Land Registry and how to obtain it*. The Land Registry's address is given at the back of the book.

Not all land is registered, and tracking down the owner can be tricky. Start by asking around in the neighbourhood.

This useful leaflet is published by the Land Registry and contains information on finding the owners of registered land.

Explanatory Leaflet

No. 15

The Open Register - A guide to information held by the Land Registry and how to obtain it

Application for an
**Official Search
of the Index Map** (Note 1)

HM Land Registry

Form
96.

(Rule 9 Land Registration (Open Register)
Rules 1991)

FOR EXPLANATORY NOTES SEE OVERLEAF
Please complete in typescript or in BLACK BLOCK LETTERS all details
within the thick black lines.

To _____ District Land Registry

(Note 2)

I

of

(enter name and address of person or firm making the application)

apply for an official search of the Index Map or General Map
and Parcels Index, and the list of pending applications for
first registration, in respect of the land referred to below and
shown [_____] on the attached plan.

NOTE - Any attached plan must contain sufficient details of the
surrounding roads and other features to enable the land to be identified
satisfactorily on the Ordnance Survey Map. However, a plan may be
unnecessary if the land can be identified by postal description. Nevertheless,
the Chief Land Registrar reserves the right to ask for a plan to be supplied
where he considers it necessary.

For official use only

Description		Date

Fees Debited £			Record of Fees paid

PAYMENT OF FEE (Note 4)

Please enter X in the appropriate box:-

☐ the Land Registry fee of £ [____] accompanies this application,

or

☐ please debit the Credit Account mentioned below with the
appropriate fee payable under the current Land Registration
Fees Order.

**FOR COMPLETION
BY APPLICANTS WHO
ARE CREDIT
ACCOUNT HOLDERS**

YOUR KEY NUMBER:-

YOUR REFERENCE:-

Signed

Date

Telephone No.

Reference

HM Land Registry

Property

Postal number or description	
Name of road	
Name of locality	
Town	
Postcode	
District or London Borough	
Administrative County	
Ordnance Survey Map Reference	(Note 3)
Known Title Number(s)	

Enter Name and either address including postcode OR (if applicable)
DX number of the person to whom the official certificate of result of
search is to be sent.

Reference	

**CERTIFICATE OF RESULT OF OFFICIAL SEARCH OF
THE INDEX MAP**   **(Form 96 Result)**

It is certified that the official search applied for has been made with the
following result :- (**Only the statements opposite the boxes marked X apply.**)

☐ The land _____
   is not registered. (Note 5)

☐ The land_____
   is not affected by any caution against first registration
   or any priority notice.

☐ The land_____
   is affected by a pending application for first registration
   under the following reference _____

☐ The land_____
   is registered freehold under Title No
   _____

☐ The land_____
   is registered leasehold under Title No
   _____

☐ The land_____
   is affected by a rentcharge under Title No _____

☐ The land_____
   is affected by a caution against first registration/
   priority notice under Title No _____

Official stamp

When applying for first
registration of the above
property or writing in
relation to it, please
enclose this result of
search and any plan
annexed thereto.

These Scandia Hus homes are in perfect harmony with their sites.

Assessing land

How can you assess whether a piece of land has possible building potential? By looking – if you can – at the local Development Plan for the area, which is produced by the district council.

As a result of a change in planning law in 1991, all local councils must produce Development Plans; about half have already done so; but all councils must issue them by 1996.

Development Plans, put simply, are statements of what local authorities would like to see developed in their areas (homes, schools, roads, industrial units, etc.). Planning applications can then be matched against the Development Plan.

So by studying the Development Plan, you should have a very good idea of how the local council is going to feel about your own ideas for development.

Existing properties

Some of the very best sites are those which already have houses on them. The existing houses tend to be old, in poor condition, and basically unmortgageable. They are frequently local eyesores, and often the local council will be prepared to consider a one-for-one application, allowing a new house to be built as a replacement.

Tread carefully, however. Sometimes the local authority will insist that the old property is demolished first (so if you had been planning to camp out in it for a time, you will have to think again). Usually, it will insist that it is demolished as soon as possible after the replacement house is completed. If the original house was very small, the local authority may not want the new one to be as large as perhaps you would like it to be. All this is an area where negotiation, patience and diplomacy are essential.

Generally speaking, though, if your heart is set on building in the countryside, finding an old shack which has had a history of residential use, on a rural plot could be your best bet.

Site problems

Some years ago, my husband and I found what seemed to be a wonderful plot. It consisted of a large 18 acre field with gorgeous views and no mains services. It was set at the end of a track right in the middle of commonland in which gorse and heather grew. There was no planning permission, which was why the previous owners were selling,

because after several attempts, they had not been able to get beyond a temporary consent for a caravan which they were allowed to use for daytime accommodation only.

The local authorities insisted that owners of the field would have to prove beyond any doubt, over a number of years, that any house on the site could be justified in terms of agricultural need (not easy on just 18 acres).

I am ashamed to admit that my husband and I (but we were very young!) were completely undaunted by all this. The views from this plot were, after all, delicious! We pressed ahead with our purchase. It was a very dry summer, and pretty often, the commonland all round caught fire. We remained undaunted. Our purchase fell through only at the very last moment when our solicitor discovered an access problem in the form of a blackmail, or ransom, strip and advised us in no uncertain terms not to proceed. Blackmail strips are commonly ribbons of land right round a plot, or simply over the entrance, which are retained by a previous owner. They are usually for sale at an extortionate amount!

Ours was an example of what you might call a difficult site: in fact, just about every possible contra-indication was there, which is why it's such a good example of what not to buy – unless, of course, you are a natural martyr who happens to like years of hardship, discomfort and the risk of repeatedly unsuccessful planning applications.

Personally, every time I go past that site, I offer up silent prayers of relief. (Sometimes I can't think why – our next plot, which we did buy, was in its own way equally challenging!)

Nowadays, I'm older and wiser, and I frequently urge self builders to be very careful. There are many pitfalls in plot purchasing.

The first is that land is often advertised as a potential plot, or even as a plot. It isn't a plot unless it already has planning permission, and unless you are the kind of person who likes to bet on which raindrop will be first down the window pane, don't take chances on potential. The golden rule is that the planning permission you want should always be in place before you buy a plot at building land prices.

Problems that should be particularly avoided, apart from lack of planning permission, are to do with agricultural land, access, lack of services, drains crossing the site, and covenants.

Covenants are legal conditions which have been placed on the land. For instance, a covenant may have been placed on a plot once owned by a temperance society, specifically forbidding the development of a public house on the land; or there may be a covenant on the land forbidding development of any kind.

In some cases, covenants may be 'bought off', but take a solicitor's advice. Some covenants are pretty absurd, having been placed by people long dead, and often relating to other properties long demolished. In such cases, a solicitor might be able to advise taking out an indemnity against that covenant ever being re-enacted. Other covenants might be impossible to get round, particularly if they are recent and do specifically forbid building a new house on the site.

Drains may have to be diverted. Services can be extraordinarily expensive to bring on site, and access can be a real problem – remember, it isn't just a question of being able to get on to the site in future, but of being able to bring very large lorries, bearing timber frames and readymix cement, on to it. Footpaths and bridle paths can also be very problematic. They might cross the land, bringing with them regular invasions of ramblers and riders; worse still, what looks like a drive might in reality be only a bridle path, with no access permissible for vehicles. Watch it! These things can and do happen.

When buying a plot, treat it as though you were buying a ready-built house. Check out the neighbours – are they the Addams family? Is there going to be a gipsy site or a stone crushing plant up the road? Make as many inquiries as possible, get your solicitor to do all the usual searches, make sure you know what is in any Local Plan, talk to local people and read the local paper.

Another particularly important thing to beware of when you buy a plot is entering into building agreements with the seller. If the plot does have planning permission, its sale should not be contingent on who does the building.

Beware generally of finding plots through deals. There have been several cases of individuals purchasing plots where a developer had hoped to build three, four or even more houses, but had been unable to proceed. The site purchaser then tries to sell off the other plots, often trying to instigate financial arrangements, and organise site access and other infrastructure. Whether you are the Mr Big in all this, or one of the other purchasers, extreme caution is necessary. This kind of arrangement requires a lot of trust, mutual financial solvency, and the ability for everyone to progress in similar timescales.

The hidden costs

Even if you have a site with outline planning permission, you are by no means guaranteed plain sailing. Taking professional advice is obviously a sensible precaution, but there are also other hidden costs.

- First, you may need the site **valued** for borrowing purposes. You can expect to pay the building society around £150 for this.

- You could also have a services, level and dimensional **survey** carried out. A chartered surveyor would probably charge between £200 and £350. This survey is worth having, since it gives you literally the lie of the land and exact measurements, and it highlights potential difficulties.

- **Soil investigations** carried out by structural engineers – see also Chapter 12 – will indicate what kind of foundations you will need, which will allow you to have an accurate idea as to their cost. Soil investigations cost up to £600. A chartered surveyor is the best person to advise whether such an investigation should be carried out, and should be able to recommend someone to do it.

- **Legal fees:** the conveyance of your plot will come to around £500 to £750, depending on how much work is involved for your solicitor.

- Getting detailed **planning permission and Building Regulations** approval from the respective departments of the local district or borough authority, will also cost you money: currently, it costs £115 to apply for the former, and Building Regulations will cost £66 to get your plans checked, and a further £175 for subsequent site inspections.

From the above figures, you will see it is very easy to spend at least £1,800 before a brick has been laid. Make sure you calculate your hidden costs accurately and budget for them.

Chapter 4: Planning

Getting planning permission for a timber frame house is no different from obtaining it for any other kind of home. The planning authority is interested only in whether a building should be built at all on a specific site and in its size and appearance.

Generally, neither the internal layout nor the method of construction will be considered by the planners. However, if you are planning to build close to neighbours whose privacy is a consideration, the planners may not like windows to be sited so that you overlook next door's property. The method of construction would not normally be a factor, unless it affected the external appearance of your house – for example, if you were planning to build in aluminium.

Both internal layout and method of construction are, however, matters for Building Regulations, as we'll see later. For the moment, if you are a novice in these things, all you need to know is that as well as getting planning permission, you will also need Building Regulations approval. Until you have both, you cannot start building.

There are basically two levels of planning permission:

• **Outline consent**

• **Detailed consent**

Outline consent is an agreement in principle to allow development on a particular plot of land. Detailed or full consent means the local planning authority has agreed to allow building work to start on a specific design and size of property.

Outline planning consent is not mandatory or essential and can actually be missed out altogether if a detailed application is made straightaway.

Most outline consents will be subject to reserved matters, which means that all the major factors such as style of house, siting, access and materials to be used internally have to be agreed at the detailed stage.

Generally, if you have outline planning permission, then you have three years in which to apply for approval of reserved matters or to put in for detailed planning permission. If you have won detailed planning permission, then it has a shelf life of five years. This is the timescale in which you must start building, although there may be some cases in

which the planning authority imposes a condition that you must start sooner.

You do not have to own a piece of land to apply for planning permission on it. So if you are interested in buying a plot, but want to ensure that you can get the appropriate planning permission first, there is nothing to stop you approaching the owner of the land and making an offer to purchase, subject to winning planning consent.

You will need to get the appropriate planning application forms from the planning department of your local district or borough council. Applying will cost you (current prices) £115 for a plot of up to quarter of an acre. If you do not already own the land, you must notify the owner on a form also available from the planning department.

The owner, together with neighbours, the parish council and any other interested bodies who will be notified of your application by the planning department, will be given the chance to express an opinion.

It is a golden rule to talk to the planning officers at the local council. They will be a mine of local knowledge and will usually take an objective view of your proposals rather than a N.I.M.B.Y. (Not In My Back Yard) attitude. If you are employing an architect or other professional you can (almost) always rely on them to consult with the authority. Most will welcome you along to any such meeting which will help you to understand the whole process. This early meeting will also elicit very often vital nuggets of information such as any restrictions on the style and size of house permissible - for example, bungalows might not be allowed or country plots might have an agricultural occupancy condition. This means that the house can only be occupied by genuine farm or horticultural workers. It is not enough to keep a few chickens. You have to prove that most, if not all, of your income comes from agricultural activity.

Expect some local opposition. People do not generally like new houses in their neighbourhoods, so be prepared for their objections and try not to take them personally. Even where neighbours have fought a plan tooth and nail, they have offered friendship later. Keep this in mind. Knock on neighbours' doors; show them the plans, and

When assessing a potential plot, do bear in mind that you will need access and enough physical room in which to build.

explain what you hope to achieve. Be polite and even prepared to compromise. Above all, recognise and respect their right to express their views. Contact the local councillor and brief him or her, too with a view to getting their support.

As already indicated, planning permissions have a finite life. If you fail to seek approval for reserved matters or make a detailed application, or start building within the prescribed time limits, the consent lapses. This means making a new planning application. It is far better to renew a planning application before it lapses, as this effectively removes any reasons for refusal. With any planning permission, there is one golden rule: read the conditions attached to your consent. All permissions have a number of conditions placed on them, all need to be adhered to, and some of them can cause difficulty. Check that you are happy with the conditions, that you understand them, and that they can all be met.

But what happens if the local planning authority refuses planning permission? Well, you could give up there and then; you could try again with a new application; or you could go to appeal.

Going to appeal

If you are dissatisfied with the outcome of a planning application, you can appeal to the Secretary of State for the Environment. You can appeal against outright refusal of an outline or detailed application; or you can appeal against conditions placed on the approval (for example, on the size of house you are allowed to build); you may also go to appeal if the application has not been decided within the two-month statutory period.

Until 1991, about 40 per cent of all appeals were successful, so the odds were only slightly weighted against you. It is fair to say that the odds will now have lengthened very considerably, due to the 1991 Planning and Compensation Act.

Described as one of the most significant changes in planning law this century, the effect of the Act has been to change the ground rules by insisting that all local authorities prepare Local Plans, specifying where developments should go, and of what type.

Until 1991, planning was at best a lottery and at worst, anarchy. Major planning decisions were being made on appeal. This is now changed, because Local Plans have become the laid down planning policy for the area.

If your planning application is in accordance with the Local Plan, it will obviously stand a good chance of success. However, it is still up to the local planners to place their own interpretation on individual applications in the context of the Local Plan, and they do still have the power to reject it. Furthermore, Local Plans are, so far as self builders are concerned, painted with bold brush strokes, and tend not to show individual building plots.

That does not mean that the local planners do not welcome individual applications. However, it follows that if your application is in clear breach of the Local Plan, because for example you want to build on an area that is allocated as open space, then it will be rejected for that reason; and obviously your chances of a successful appeal will be diminished.

Of course, you are still allowed to appeal. But bear in mind that the whole idea of the 1991 Act was to reduce the number of appeals and make them a less attractive means of recourse.

Remember this before committing yourself to an appeal. If you possibly can, avoid one by taking time and care to identify the right plot and submit the right application in the first place. Individual building plots can be found – often as infill, and sometimes within or immediately adjoining small rural settlements.

Seeing through a successful application will involve negotiating with the local planning officer from the outset. Once you have submitted your application, keep tabs on it. If you scent refusal, ask for the application to be deferred so that you can modify it and, with no history of refusal on the site, you can resubmit an application which is more likely to succeed.

Even if an application is refused, it is still worth negotiating and trying again with an amended plan. Obviously throughout all this, it will help to be as reasonable, flexible and polite as possible. Your object is, after all, to submit an application which the planning officer will support when it reaches the committee.

If all fails, what then? After you get your official notice of refusal, you have six months in which to appeal. The appeal itself could take up to nine months before there is a decision. Appeals sound daunting, but a lot depends on how they are handled. You, as the appellant, can opt to have it dealt with by either a written representations procedure, or a hearing (a third option is a full-blown public inquiry, but it is unlikely that a self builder after an individual plot would want or be granted this).

Both written representations and hearings are relatively informal procedures, although having got this far, you would be strongly advised to get good professional advice.

Any appeal is dealt with by an appeals inspector, who acts on behalf of the Secretary of the State for the Environment, and who has the power to confirm, vary or completely change the council's decision. The inspector's decision is final. It can be challenged in the courts but only on a point of law.

Do your homework before an appeal.

- **Look at how other planning appeals have been handled. Inspect minutes of council meetings, and look for actual letters from planning inspectors giving their decisions. Note the references in these letters; you can then ask to inspect the actual appeal letters, and see how they were lodged.**

- **Assemble your arguments so that you can present a really good case.**

- **Attend planning committee meetings and know exactly how your application was handled and what was said when it was rejected.**

- **Know the Local Plan inside out because that, after all, is the central issue. Can you argue that your own application is in accord with it? Or have you a really good case to challenge the planners' decision?**

You can, as already explained, appeal if the planning committee fails to give you a decision. When an application is received, the council must acknowledge it and give the date by which it has a statutory obligation to issue a decision. If it has not issued its decision by then, you can appeal.

However, most planning departments are snowed under. The chances are that the planning officer will already have sent back a letter with its acknowledgement saying that the department is under pressure and asking you to agree an extension. It's probably diplomatic to do so, but what if time is not on your side?

If you are anxious to get a decision, explain your circumstances to the planning officer. You can always enter a planning appeal on the basis of non-determination, but going to appeal does take time. Diplomatic negotiation, even if it requires patience, will probably be much more effective.

An appeal against refusal begins with written submissions. First, it is your turn.

The council have four weeks to answer this, and you will then receive a copy of their written statement and have two weeks in which to reply to it. After this exchange of statements, you decide on what basis to decide the appeal.

Whether written representations, a public inquiry or an informal inquiry are held, the inspector will pay a site visit. It could be unaccompanied or one which both you and the council will attend.

During this site visit, no further arguments should be made by either side. You are only allowed to answer questions or point out to the inspector things you have already put in your written evidence (for instance, *"This is the site of my proposed access, as you will see from my previous submission."*). After this site visit, everyone will troop off in their separate cars and another silence will ensue. A month or so later, you will receive the inspector's findings. If you have won, you have your planning consent.

Part 2
Choices

Self build is all about freedom of choice, but it is important that every choice made is an informed one. In this section, we look at the spectrum of choices in every phase of the project, from choosing a timber frame and the design, to the various ways of managing a self build.

Chapter 5: Matters financial

People usually give two reasons for wanting to self build.

- **To save money**
- **To get exactly the house they want**

It can be very hard to quantify what 'saving money' actually means; one man's saving will often be another person's overspend. It is also quite often the case that 'saving money' is not the main object at all – getting a house built to the highest possible specification, within budget, is a much more accurate way to express the true goal of most self builders.

That said, the usual rule of thumb is that a self built house will have on completion a market value that is 20 to 30 per cent greater than the cost of the build (including the cost of plot).

The savings it is possible to make are demonstrated by the figures below, quoted by leading timber frame company Medina Gimson. The figures are for building costs alone (ie, materials and labour) and do not include the price of the land.

- **Self build** A: Managing the entire build yourself and doing a fair amount of the labour: £28 per square foot
- **Self build B:** Managing the build yourself, employing sub-contractors, and playing a management role: £32 per square foot
- **Self Build C:** Using a building contractor: £37-£40 per square foot
- **Not self build (D):** Were you simply to purchase a house, you can expect to pay £45 to £50 a square foot.

These figures are by no means set in stone. It is possible to spend more (quite a lot more, if you have expensive tastes) by specifying a top-of-the-range kitchen and high quality fittings. Nevertheless, it's instructive to take these figures and use them as a starting point for calculating a few more sums, again excluding the cost of the land.

A 1,500 square foot house would cost £74,700 to buy. This figure allows the developer to pay for his overheads and make a profit (D).

Self builder (C) would be able to reduce this to £64,700; but by managing your build (A or B) the figure could fall as low as £45,000.

Savings are there to be made. But they will not simply fall into your lap. They will have to be strategically planned.

This really cannot be emphasised enough. The most financially successful self builds are always those that are masterminded well in advance, right down to the last detail.

Here are some guidelines which have been common links in successful builds.

- **Sell any previous house first**
- **Don't pay too much for the plot – negotiate if necessary.**
- **Shop around for your timber frame package**
- **Allow a good, healthy sum for contingencies so that there is no question of running out of money if something early on in the build goes over budget**
- **Be wary of over-specifying on the finishing touches – if you want to spend £40,000 on a fabulous designer kitchen, a dream bathroom and gold-plated taps in the utility room, that's your choice. But, if you are not careful, this is where your money runs away with you.**

Budget

The first thing you need to do is set your budget. This will depend on your equity (probably from the sale of your last home plus any savings, windfalls, etc) and the mortgage you are likely to get for your self build.

Let us assume that you have an overall budget of £120,000. This is a sum which may well seem too high for some readers of this book, and more like peanuts to some others. But whatever your own budget is, the principles of allocating it are the same.

Subtract ten per cent at once from your budget to give you a safety margin for contingencies. This may seem like a lot to you, and indeed some advisors consider that five per cent is ample for a contingency. Really, it is up to you to decide – but do bear in mind that unexpectedly difficult foundations can swallow up your money. Put your contingency away in a safe place, such as a building society account, and forget you have it. With any luck, you will not need to touch it until the build is over. If it is still lying in your account, you will be able to treat yourself to some fabulous new furniture, and maybe that dream bathroom after all.

This leaves you with £108,000 to spend, with a safety net of £12,000. From this £108,000, you will need to subtract a large enough sum to pay for the following: services (water, drainage, gas, electricity, telephone); fees to the local authority for planning and Building Regulations approval; legal fees (conveyancing); other professional fees (eg, architect, surveyor); guarantee (Foundation 15, NHBC, architect's certification); and site insurances (to protect you against claims for injury, or theft, from the site during the build); other (eg, storage of furniture while you build, renting somewhere to live while you build).

Only you can do these sums; what matters is that you do them, because so many self builders forget to put them in their budget at all, and then wonder why they seem to have overspent!

The cost of services, particularly of water connection, varies sharply over the country; another great variable is the amount you will be paying in legal and professional fees. You can probably expect to pay around £1,250 for a building guarantee, and a further £400 for site insurances. Only you know whether you are going to have to put your furniture into storage and spend money on rent. Do your homework first, cost everything in, and come up with a realistic sum.

For the sake of this exercise, we will allow £8,000 to cover these indirect building costs, so that you are now left with £100,000 to pay for your dream home. We will also assume for the sake of this exercise that you do not plan to build a garage – yet, at least. If, in reality, you do intend to include a garage in your build, then remember to cost this in.

So, assuming no garage, how much of your £100,000 should be allocated to the plot? There are two ways to begin working this out. First, ask yourself the size of house you want to build. Assuming it is going to be 1,600 square foot, and you intend managing the build yourself, and allowing a reasonable standard of specification, you could allow £35 per square foot. Thus, your home would cost you £56,000 to build, leaving £44,000 for the plot.

A more realistic starting point for most people is to work out first how much they need to pay for their plot, and then take their calculations from there. A rough and ready formula is one third for the plot, one third for building materials, and one third for labour. This does not always apply, but it should give you a starting point.

In some parts of the country, high land prices distort the third-third-third principle, and you could expect to spend at least 50 per cent (and in London and Home Counties, even more than that) of your overall budget on a plot. In other parts of the country, land prices are lower, and you might need to allocate only 25 per cent of your proposed budget to a plot purchase. A lot also depends on the size and siting of the plot. All you can do at this early planning stage is look around your chosen locality, and decide on the likely plot price. Take this sum away from your budget total.

If you are lucky, your research will show that you will be able to buy a plot for exactly £44,000. This leaves you with the amount you will have available with which to build – £56,000. This would allow you to build your 1,600 square foot house at £35 a square foot. If your researches show that you are going to have to pay £54,000 for a plot, you could build a 1,300 square foot home at £35 a square foot. If you live in a part of the country where land prices are cheap, you may be able to pick up a plot for £30,000, which would allow you to build a 2,000 square foot house at £35 a square foot.

Early planning

Just as there are many ways to crack an egg, so are there many ways of getting a timber frame home built. Do explore and cost out the options. These include:

- Going to a manufacturer and ordering from their standard ranges

- Going to a manufacturer with your own design and getting their architectural services to draw it up

- Going to an architect of your own, and then sourcing a manufacturer

- Using a design/consultancy service with no manufacturing plant of their own, but who will source you a timber frame

> **Consider the cost of erecting the frame.**
> **Your choices include:**
>
> - Having your supplier both deliver and erect the frame
>
> - Having the frame supplied only, and put up by independent erectors
>
> **The best advice? It's always worth getting a quote.**

Whatever way you decide to go about it, the biggest part of your building budget will be the amount allocated for the timber frame itself.

Prices vary staggeringly, and different components come with different packages, some far better value than others. Send off for as many brochures as possible. Most will quote costs per square foot. Be careful with these figures. Your aim is to compare projected costs for materials and labour – in other words, what the house will actually cost to build. Unfortunately, what the manufacturers mean is often not entirely clear.

- Costs per square foot relate to **habitable space,** ie the floor area measured from the inside of the internal leaf. The measurement should not be taken from the external leaf, but nevertheless this is what is sometimes quoted. Obviously, it artificially distorts the true size of the house, and its price per square foot. If you are not absolutely sure, ask!

- Costs per square foot should never include a **garage.** This is because a garage is cheap to build per square foot, and so if a 400 square foot garage is included in the costings, it will artificially bring down the price.

- Ask if the quoted cost per square foot includes **services,** such as gas and electricity. Some manufacturers include these; others do not. Again, if you are not sure, ask.

- Does the projected cost per square foot mean a house that is completely habitable, or does it mean one which will require **further expenditure.** Does it, for instance, include a fitted kitchen and bathrooms? Or any (or all) flooring? A central heating system? Or any extras, such as a heat exchange unit, or a clothes drying cabinet? And what is the specification of the actual frame itself and the insulation?

This cannot be the complete list by any means; but they are the main areas of confusion. Ask what assumptions the suppliers are making when they quote a price per square foot, and then ask yourself whether their idea of a finished house is yours!

Specification

Specification is important. Most Scandinavian timber frames are six inches thick, as opposed to four inches, and so they have correspondingly more room for greater insulation. Furthermore, when Scandinavian manufacturers quote square footage, they are quoting for a virtually complete house, including a fully fitted kitchen, flooring in all rooms, and a heat recovery unit. Scandinavian kit houses are often 'turn key' builds as well, which means that the house is completely built for you, and all you have to do is turn the key and walk in.

By contrast, when seemingly low prices per square foot are quoted, ask exactly what is meant. Often, there is no catch but sometimes it pays to be sceptical.

Materials

The main variable is the materials used. Let's go back to our 1,500 square foot house which, as we have already seen, could cost the self build manager anywhere from £45,000 to £60,000. The bricks for this could cost somewhere between £1,200 and £3,200; the tiles could cost from £1,200 to £4,000.

Treat costs quoted per square foot as a guide.

Costs per square foot are, in truth, best treated as a useful indication, but no more than that. The really crucial point at this stage is the kit you buy, and what comes with it. Some kits include glazing, nails, doors for built-in wardrobes, insulation and plasterboard; others do not.

Specifications for kits can run into several pages. You could also draw up your own specification and then ask several manufacturers to quote so that you can make genuinely meaningful comparisons.

The lenders

There are various ways of financing your self build, but increasingly lenders who specialise in this area will insist that you sell your existing house first.

This is not always so – if you have no charge, or only a very small mortgage, on your first property, the building society may actually prefer you to keep it on while you build as it cushions the risk in lending to you. Not only that, but it would save you money on having to rent.

Probably for most people, however, it makes far more sense to free up your capital and sell your previous home. This is to overcome two problems.

House prices are notoriously uncertain, and until you have sold your property, you will have no idea what your true equity is. The second problem is that houses can take an awfully long time to sell. This could leave you with two mortgages and two sets of council tax to pay; even a short overlap can find you having to pay through the nose for bridging finance. Never think you can cope with this. One couple who believed they would need only a very tiny mortgage, built in the garden of their existing cottage. But the cottage took a year to sell, and fetched £30,000 less than its asking price: a devastating deficit.

Having sold your home, and liberated your capital, you should now shop around the potential lenders in earnest. But first, you will need to show that you have done your sums in detail. Flaunt your budget! You should take with you details of the timber frame you hope to buy, and details of your plot and planning permission. You should also draw up a time schedule.

As for the lenders themselves, none, you will be pleased to hear, should be in the least bit concerned that you are planning to build a timber frame house. It will make no difference at all to their willingness (or otherwise) to advance you money – although it may make a difference as to the timing of the payments if you take out a staged mortgage, in which the money is released at fixed stages of the build. More of that in a moment. What matters now and makes the difference between a successful application for a loan and an unsuccessful one, is the financial preparation you have done, right down to the last detail.

Lenders will also be anxious to hear that your build will be professionally supervised, so be ready to supply details of the Foundation 15 scheme, your architect, NHBC builder, or whatever.

The vital point to be considered which is peculiar to timber frame construction is this stage payment business. The golden rule in self building is never to pay money up-front, either for supplies or for sub-contracted labour. And yet most timber frame suppliers like all of the money up-front.

In other words, they like you to pop a cheque in the post with your order.

The manufacturers argue, with some reason, that the house is being made especially for an individual customer. However, customers do not expect to pay in full for something that has yet to be made, delivered and found satisfactory – especially when there is no guarantee of their money being refunded if the unthinkable happens, and the company goes bust.

This 'money first' attitude goes against the whole grain of consumer thinking. And disaster has happened! One couple paid a timber frame company £25,000 on a Thursday. The company crashed the following Monday, and the couple lost their money. It might not happen often, but even so, be warned!

The building societies certainly do not like this payment up front business, and will quite simply not play along with it. They will not release a stage payment until the timber frame has been manufactured and delivered; they may not even release the payment until the frame has been actually (and satisfactorily) erected. So is this an impasse?

No. The way round it is to offer a legal agreement. You pay the money to your solicitor, who guarantees to hand it over when the timber frame is delivered. This gives the timber frame company the assurance they need, keeps the lender happy, and is also more satisfactory for the self builder. Keep this arrangement in mind when talking to building societies or banks.

Building societies

Some building societies have tailor-made packages for self-builders, usually called Progress Mortgages. All lenders will carry out stringent checks, and will normally advance the funds in four or five stages as the build progresses. You will not be able to get a 100 per cent mortgage on the project. Some lenders will advance 75 per cent of the value of the plot, and 100 per cent of the building costs; others will lend up to 75 per cent of the total value of the finished project.

Some lenders will charge normal rates, others will charge more, for instance somewhere between one and 2.5 per cent over variable mortgage rate while building is in progress, with the loading taken off when building has finished. This may not be such bad news as it sounds – if you are a new borrower with the building society, you may be entitled to the first year discount offered, which can knock out the extra loading.

One specific point to note with building societies is that most like the timber frame not only delivered but erected satisfactorily before releasing the appropriate stage payment.

Banks

Banks are very well worth talking to if you are planning a self build. It is not uncommon for the majority of self build projects to be backed by a bank rather than a building society. Banks may lend while building takes place; you would then convert the loan to a standard mortgage on completion.

Living in the interim

One final word in this section. If you have sold your previous home, you will need somewhere to live while you build, so count this into your financial reckoning unless you move in rent-free with friends or family. If not, you must allow for rent for a home or caravan. A caravan on site will probably need temporary planning permission so check with your planning authority first. Some caravan companies will do a sale and return deal for self builders.

Costs

The following charts are not intended to be exhaustive (if they were, they'd fill this book all by themselves). They are, however, intended to provide you with a framework.

First, how should you choose a timber frame? Here are questions it is suggested you ask suppliers so that you can weigh up the cost implications when you are comparing kit prices and specifications from different manufacturers.

Choosing a timber frame

Size of house _____

Supplier _____

_____

_____

_____

Cost as supplied _____
(per square foot)

Thickness of the frame? _____

Does the kit include?

Basic frame   Yes _____ No _____   If no, cost implication   £_____

External wall panels   Yes _____ No _____   If no, cost implication   £_____
(including breather
membrane)

Internal wall panels   Yes _____ No _____   If no, cost implication   £_____

Floor joists   Yes _____ No _____   If no, cost implication   £_____

Floor decking   Yes _____ No _____   If no, cost implication   £_____

External doors   Yes _____ No _____   If no, cost implication   £_____
and windows

Roof trusses   Yes _____ No _____   If no, cost implication   £_____

Tank platforms   Yes _____ No _____   If no, cost implication   £_____

Roof felt   Yes _____ No _____   If no, cost implication   £_____

Battens   Yes _____ No _____   If no, cost implication   £_____

Loose noggings   Yes _____ No _____   If no, cost implication   £_____

All metal connections   Yes _____ No _____   If no, cost implication   £_____
including nails, truss
clips & joist hangers etc

Fire steps   Yes _____ No _____   If no, cost implication   £_____
and safety barriers

Plasterboard   Yes _____ No _____   If no, cost implication   £_____
(state thickness)

Vapour check   Yes _____ No _____   If no, cost implication   £_____

Wall insulation   Yes _____ No _____   If no, cost implication   £_____
(state thickness)

Loft insulation   Yes _____ No _____   If no, cost implication   £_____
(state thickness)

Ground insulation   Yes _____ No _____   If no, cost implication   £_____
(state thickness)

Glazing (double/triple/ low emissivity)	Yes _____ No _____	If no, cost implication	£_____
Flooring (wood)	Yes _____ No _____	If no, cost implication	£_____
Other flooring	Yes _____ No _____	If no, cost implication	£_____
All internal joinery, **doors and linings** **including skirtings etc**	Yes _____ No _____	If no, cost implication	£_____
Fitted kitchen **including cupboard/** **wardrobe doors,** **fireplaces**	Yes _____ No _____	If no, cost implication	£_____
Heat exchanger	Yes _____ No _____	If no, cost implication	£_____
Boiler	Yes _____ No _____	If no, cost implication	£_____
Facias and soffits etc	Yes _____ No _____	If no, cost implication	£_____
Guttering and **downpipes etc**	Yes _____ No _____	If no, cost implication	£_____
Is erection of the **frame included in the** **cost of the kit?**	Yes _____ No _____	If no, cost implication	£_____
Do you want other **services managed** **and provided for you?**	Yes _____ No _____	If no, cost implication	£_____

You could also ask the following questions about the service offered by the timber frame supplier. This element does not have a direct financial cost; but it is the quality of the manufacturers' service that, time and time again, makes the difference to how successfully you can manage a self build.

Free inspection service **during the course of** **the build, as well as** **on completion?**	Yes _____ No _____	**Lists of approved** **contractors,** **recommended suppliers,** **materials, etc?**	Yes _____ No _____
Help available **quickly and when** **needed?** (ie at weekends)	Yes _____ No _____	**Willingness to introduce** **you to other self** **builders who have** **used the same kits?**	Yes _____ No _____
Advice on quantities of **materials needed?**	Yes _____ No _____		

Budgeting your build

Below you will find a draft budget. You may want a more itemised breakdown of some items, while other headings will not apply to you but this will at least supply a good starting point for calculating your costs. Take two copies of your budget.

Use the first copy to compare quotes, and to decide which parts of the build will be both supplied and fixed; where you will want to buy your own materials and sub-contract the labour; and where you will be buying the materials and doing the labour yourself.

Use the second to control your budget as the build progresses and to record VAT so that you can reclaim it when the build is completed.

Total sum available: £ _____

Minus ten per cent
contingency allowance   £ _____

Budget   £ _____

Price of plot   £ _____

Improving access   £ _____

1. Services

Mains sewerage   £ _____

Mains surface
water sewerage   £ _____

Electricity   £ _____

Gas   £ _____

Oil   £ _____

LPG   £ _____

Water   £ _____

Septic tank/other   £ _____

Telecom   £ _____

Professional   £ _____

Surveyor

Soil investigation   £ _____

Legal   £ _____

Estate agent   £ _____

Architect/engineer   £ _____

Statutory

Outline planning
application   £ _____

Full planning
application   £ _____

Planning consultant   £ _____

Building Regulations   £ _____

Plans fee   £ _____

Inspection fee   £ _____

Before building
register project for

Foundation 15   £ _____

NHBC Buildmark   £ _____

Similar warranty   £ _____

Quantity
surveyor's report   £ _____

2. Expenses for
living during build

Rent/accommodation   £ _____

Storage of furniture   £ _____

Interest   £ _____

3. Expenses of build

Quotes	1st	2nd	3rd
a. Professional			
Surveyor	£_____	£_____	£_____
Engineer	£_____	£_____	£_____
Architect	£_____	£_____	£_____

**b. Foundations and
other groundwork**

Labour   £_____ £_____ £_____

Materials   £_____ £_____ £_____

Hire of machinery   £_____ £_____ £_____

Disposal of spoil   £_____ £_____ £_____

Foul drains
to main sewer   £_____ £_____ £_____

Surface water drains
to main sewer   £_____ £_____ £_____

Services   £_____ £_____ £_____

c. Timber frame

Supply   £_____ £_____ £_____

Erection   £_____ £_____ £_____

d. Brickwork
(including fireplaces
and garden walls)

Supply and fix   £_____ £_____ £_____

Materials   £_____ £_____ £_____

Labour   £_____ £_____ £_____

Hire of scaffolding   £_____ £_____ £_____

e. Roof

Supply and fix   £_____ £_____ £_____

Materials   £_____ £_____ £_____

Labour   £_____ £_____ £_____

f. First fix

Electrics

Supply and fix   £_____ £_____ £_____

Materials   £_____ £_____ £_____

Labour   £_____ £_____ £_____

Plumbing

Supply and fix   £_____ £_____ £_____

Materials   £_____ £_____ £_____

Labour   £_____ £_____ £_____

Joinery

Supply and fix   £_____ £_____ £_____

Materials   £_____ £_____ £_____

Labour   £_____ £_____ £_____

**g. Floor insulation
and screed**

Supply and fix   £_____ £_____ £_____

Materials   £_____ £_____ £_____

Labour   £_____ £_____ £_____

**h. Wall and
loft insulation**

Supply and fix   £_____ £_____ £_____

Materials   £_____ £_____ £_____

Labour   £_____ £_____ £_____

i. Drylining

Plasterboard

Supply and fix   £_____ £_____ £_____

Materials   £_____ £_____ £_____

Labour   £_____ £_____ £_____

Jointing/taping

Supply and fix   £_____ £_____ £_____

Materials   £_____ £_____ £_____

Labour   £_____ £_____ £_____

j. Glazing

Supply and fix   £_____ £_____ £_____

Materials   £_____ £_____ £_____

Labour   £_____ £_____ £_____

k. Rainwater system
(guttering and
downpipes)

Supply and fix   £_____ £_____ £_____

Materials   £_____ £_____ £_____

Labour   £_____ £_____ £_____

l. Second fix

Electrics

Supply and fix	£_____	£_____	£_____
Materials	£_____	£_____	£_____
Labour	£_____	£_____	£_____

Plumbing

Supply and fix	£_____	£_____	£_____
Materials (bathroom and cloakroom suites, radiators, central heating boiler)	£_____	£_____	£_____
Labour	£_____	£_____	£_____

Joinery

Supply and fix	£_____	£_____	£_____
Materials	£_____	£_____	£_____
Labour	£_____	£_____	£_____

m. Decoration

Supply and fix	£_____	£_____	£_____
Materials	£_____	£_____	£_____
Labour	£_____	£_____	£_____

n. Kitchen and utility

Supply and fix	£_____	£_____	£_____
Materials	£_____	£_____	£_____
Labour	£_____	£_____	£_____

o. Fixtures and fittings

Hard flooring	£_____	£_____	£_____
Soft flooring	£_____	£_____	£_____
Curtains	£_____	£_____	£_____
Light fittings	£_____	£_____	£_____
Other	£_____	£_____	£_____

p. External works

Garage	£_____	£_____	£_____
Shed	£_____	£_____	£_____
Landscaping	£_____	£_____	£_____
Planting	£_____	£_____	£_____
Drives and paths	£_____	£_____	£_____

notes:

1. If you are intending to contribute some of your own labour, allocate a value to it equivalent to a professional labour charge. That way, you are writing in another contingency and you won't be caught on the hop if you find that you are unable to do the second fix electrics after all.

2. It is useful to compare supply and fix costs with materials, and labour. Nine times out of ten, it will be cheaper for you to buy your own materials and sub-contract the labour. But there is the odd occasion when a specialist can get hold of materials cheaper than you can.

3. Get quotes, not estimates. An estimate is what it says it is; no more than an estimate of how much a job will cost. A quote should be the exact cost.

VAT refunds for 'do-it-yourself' builders

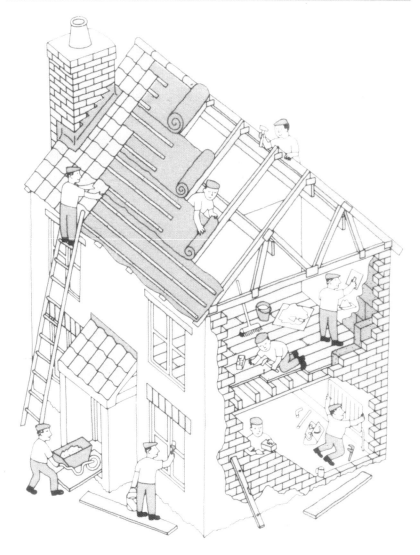

This leaflet provides invaluable information on reclaiming VAT when your self build is completed.

Keeping records

Managing the cash flow is one of the most important elements of managing the build as a whole. Cash flow can be a problem if you are having to tie in build progress with stage payments from a building society. Because a timber frame build moves so fast, you could find yourself in the position of having to make large payments up-front before the building society has agreed to release its money. It's essential to have a very detailed time schedule worked out in advance, in which you know what will be happening when, and when you need to order materials to arrive on site. It's also a very good idea to set up an account at a builder's merchant: when they know that you are likely to be spending £40,000 with them on materials, they are going to want your business. An account should give you at least a 30-day leeway in settling your bills.

Your second copy of the sample budget will help you to do just that with a few simple adjustments. This time, instead of using the column on the right hand side to compare quotes, set it out like this:

Quote, Supplier, Actual cost, VAT, Total paid, Date paid

Keep checking your quotes against the actual costs. This way you can continually control your budget and your cash flow. You could also (or instead) use a quantity surveyor to prepare regular reports.

Reclaiming VAT

This is a subject which always worries a great number of self builders. In fact, there's a theory in the self build world that VAT really stands for Vast Amount of Trouble.

The general principle is that you will have to pay Value Added Tax on the materials of a new house, but you will be able to reclaim this. VAT is not payable in the first place on labour and so you will not have to reclaim it.

It is vitally important for you, the self builder to know this, because sadly quite a few people in the building industry do not. Over and over again, I have angry readers complaining to me that their bricklayer has charged them VAT, even though they bought the bricks, and that the electrician has charged them VAT on both products and labour.

This should never arise. If you are using a sub-contractor who is not VAT registered, he should not charge you VAT. If you are using one who is VAT registered, he should be giving you a zero rated invoice, showing that there is no VAT to be paid on either labour or materials, and of course no VAT for you to reclaim.

If you are doing your own purchasing, you will be charged VAT on building materials, and allowed to reclaim it at the very end of the build. You will not be able to reclaim VAT on tools or equipment hire. You will be charged VAT for professional advice, but this is not reclaimable.

If you use sub-contractors who are not VAT registered, you should ensure that it is you who buys the materials. That way, invoices will be made out to you, and you can reclaim the VAT.

All this should be clear enough. Yet it is amazing how many sub-contractors try popping VAT on to their labour charges: they shouldn't. Let's be charitable, and assume it is a mistake on their part and not a scam. But if this happens what can you do about it? You can either: refuse to accept the invoice, and explain that you have been overcharged by (currently) 17.5 per cent, or you can withhold that amount.

If you have, out of sheer ignorance, already paid the invoice complete with VAT, go back to the sub-contractor and ask for the VAT element back. Your sub-contractor should then hand back the over-payment (whilst apologising profusely) and adjust his own VAT returns next time.

Customs and Excise will not refund VAT for you if you should not have paid it in the first place; however, you could try asking your local office for a letter outlining the position, which you could show to the sub-contractor in question. Most building sub-contractors are very unlikely to want their VAT records questioned by Customs and Excise, and hopefully the faintest prospect of this will be enough to make them hand back your money.

If your sub-contractor says 'Go away' (or similar), you will have to consider legal action. A solicitor's letter, or an action in the small claims court, should do the trick. It is a good idea to try the gentle, polite approach first.

When buying materials, all you need do is keep records and wait for the happy day when a large cheque thuds through your shiny new letter box. Put all your invoices into large box files. Make sure that each invoice is correctly addressed to you (and not, for instance, your bricklayer, who may have popped down to the local builder's merchant where you have an account, to buy a bag of cement). Make sure that the VAT element is clearly shown, ideally as a separate item, but at least put on the invoice so that you can calculate it. You must also retain all your original invoices as the VAT man will not accept photocopies.

When your build is finished, you will be able to reclaim your VAT from Customs and Excise on production of proof that your house is finished. A completion certificate from the building inspector, or your architect, or a letter from the building society, will all be acceptable proof. You must submit your claim within three months of your build's completion.

You can claim back your VAT once, and once only, after the build is finished. This is extremely unfair on self builders, since commercial builders, like all businesses, are able to re-claim VAT once every three months, and this is obviously good for anyone's cash flow. You may possibly be able to reclaim your VAT quarterly by putting it through your business accounts: for instance, if you are building a new farmhouse. However, this would not then go through the standard self build VAT system.

VAT is reclaimable on a new garage, if it is built at the same time as your house, and also on site works such as a driveway, walls, fences and patios. But beware! These must all be finished before you have completion on your new house. Obviously, VAT can amount to a lot of money, so it's worth pressing on with work to get back as much as you possibly can.

As I have said, VAT is refundable to self builders on virtually all building products, including your timber frame, bricks, tiles, plasterboard and so on. After that, it becomes less obvious and what is and isn't allowable changes all the time. You can get VAT back on fixed flooring (quarry tiles, for instance), but not on carpet. As a rule of thumb, VAT is refundable on anything that goes into your home that you would not be able to take with you when you move. Until very recently, you could reclaim VAT on a fitted kitchen but not on fitted wardrobes in a bedroom. This was successfully challenged by a major developer – and self builders can reap the benefit.

General advice is to keep all your invoices, even the ones where a VAT refund is questionable: you may be in for a pleasant surprise.

There is a very helpful leaflet, Notice 719, on how self builders can reclaim VAT. It is a model of plain English and you can get one simply by phoning the local Customs and Excise office whose number is in your phone book. Get a copy before you even start.

Chapter 6: Meet the professionals!

This book is aimed at people who want to manage the builds of their own homes. But most of us are amateurs!

We can't lay bricks; more importantly, we can't tell whether someone else is laying the bricks badly or well. And because we're amateurs, we are vulnerable: natural prey in the hands of any cowboy builder out to make his money.

The self builder is often the only amateur on site and yet also the boss. In such a situation, it's easy to lack confidence. But cheer up. First, all self builders learn quickly. Secondly, there are professionals to help you.

Make allies of these, use them properly, and you immediately improve your chances of a successful self build.

Let's meet the ones a self builder is most likely to need.

The Estate Agent

Estate agents are not particularly involved in the selling of individual plots to self builders. But they can come up trumps, so if you are looking for land in a particular area, register with as many different estate agents as you can find, and remind them once a week that you are still looking.

The Solicitor

You will need a solicitor to handle the purchase of your plot of land for you, making all the necessary legal searches. You may also need a solicitor as the build progresses, notably to handle the transfer of money for the timber frame, and possibly (though hopefully it won't be necessary) to fire off fierce solicitor's letters to any sub-contractor or supplier who hasn't come up to scratch.

ESTATE AGENT

SOLICITOR

SURVEYOR

The Surveyor

A surveyor is in many ways the ultimate property professional. In some ways, his role is that of estate agent, engineer and architect combined. A chartered surveyor will examine your chosen building plot for you; arrange soil samples and advise on foundations; handle your planning application; come up with working drawings; and can even supervise your build for you, giving certificates at each stage of completion. A chartered surveyor will also do your setting out – marking out the exact area on the ground where your house is going to be built.

The Quantity Surveyor

A quantity surveyor is a must. A quantity surveyor will quantify exactly what materials you need to order; how many, how much and when. A quantity surveyor's report is worth its weight in gold, partly because it helps you order materials exactly (instead of by guesswork), and partly because it helps you keep track of costs.

The Engineer

There seem to be engineers in every corner of human activity these days, and the self build site is no exception. A structural engineer can advise on site difficulties, and will design foundations. You may not need an engineer; but if you have a difficult sloping site, or one on exceptionally sticky clay, an engineer may be a good idea. Your architect, surveyor, or the building inspector, will advise as to whether you should get an engineer.

The Architect

Architects, as we all know, drive Citroën cars, have beards, read *The Guardian,* are married to social workers, and wear glasses and bow ties. This is a tired old cliché and not always true. Nevertheless, I was delighted when ours turned up in a trusty Citroën. He even had a beard. But let's be serious. There are architects and architects. Changes are afoot but a 'real' architect has studied seven years, and is registered with The Architects Registration Council of the United Kingdom, before joining the Royal Institute of British Architects (RIBA).

QUANTITY SURVEYOR

ENGINEER

ARCHITECT

The RIBA has a list of architects interested in private, individual houses as well as booklets about how to choose and commission an architect.

Nothing beats an architect-designed house, specifically designed for individual clients and an individual site, and there are some splendid examples in timber frame. Nor is using an architect necessarily a tremendous expense: professional expertise can and often does save money, and anyway, most architects are not sticklers for the fixed fee which the RIBA suggests. Most will negotiate their charges.

You may also get non-RIBA members offering 'architectural services', which suggests that they are not qualified to be registered. That doesn't always mean they are not very good; it just means you should be cautious. Check out their previous work, and talk to former clients.

Architects are useful to self builders in one, two or all of three ways.

Design: The title 'architect designed house' has a certain cachet; as suggested, there is no reason why you shouldn't get an architect to design you a house, and then get this design made up in timber frame.

Supervision: Architects supervise the build at the level you agree. He or she could take over part or all of the entire project, and manage it for you, handling everything from getting the planning permission to final completion.

Certification: A good way for self build managers to use an architect is to agree that he or she will make a specific number of visits at key points during the build, check progress, and also certificate the build. You may find that someone who simply offers 'architectural services' will not be qualified to do this.

A key point in using surveyors, quantity surveyors, engineers or architects, is to check their professional indemnity so that your home is guaranteed against defects in the future. Ensure that the indemnity is going to be enough to cover your house – architect's professional insurance is expensive, but as the client, you could foot the bill for increasing the cover on your own house. The indemnity usually lasts for 15 years; if during this time, your

MARRIAGE COUNSELLOR

BUILDING INSPECTOR

professional dies, any claims could be made against the estate. A special indemnity scheme exists for exactly that purpose, by which the widow and family of an architect can insure against that possibility.

One other point: if you use an architect or surveyor to supervise and certificate your build, make sure he or she has experience of timber frame. What do you mean, you don't know? Ask!

The Building Inspector

A building inspector is a key figure during the build of your house. He is there to ensure that you adhere to all Building Regulations, and he will pay regular site visits.

You will need Building Regulations approval of the various calculations for the structure of your timber frame home, from foundations to the roof. Never start building until you have this approval.

To apply for this, you can either wait for detailed planning permission to come through, or apply for it at the same time. Get the right form (from the building control department of your local council), and send it off with the fees and two sets of plans, and any other drawings required. You will need to pay one set of fees to lodge your plans for Building Regulations approval; and another set for inspection.

When approval is granted, you will receive cards to send to the building inspector whenever certain stages of the build are being reached.

The basic job of the building inspector is to check and approve the plans, and then to make sure that the work actually complies with them. Most of the inspections are at an early stage of the build, to do with foundations and drains, and you are not allowed to cover these in until they have been inspected. A missed inspection can achieve a massive rating on the nuisance scale, resulting in wasted time and money. If you are managing your build, make sure that the building inspector is duly notified in good time before each visit.

The building inspector is responsible for a great deal, including structural stability, moisture content of the building, ventilation, insulation, staircases, chimneys, and all sanitary aspects.

A building inspector can be friend or foe. He may look as though he is a fresh faced and callow youth straight from college; but treat him with respect.

His word goes. If he tells you to dig down another metre, smile and do so – even if the engineer's report said otherwise. As a matter of fact, this happened to us, but then the engineer's report had identified some nearby trees as hawthorns; when the building inspector turned up, he correctly spotted that they were in fact oaks. And equally correctly, ordered the foundations to go deeper.

Make an ally of the building inspector. His help can be invaluable, and of all the professionals you will come across, he is in many ways the one who matters most.

The Marriage Counsellor

Self building can be a strain on relationships. It has been known for couples to build their dream house only to get divorced soon afterwards.

How can you avoid having to call in Relate? First, share the same vision; if you don't, you're unlikely to share the same commitment when the build starts.

Secondly, it will help if living conditions during the build aren't too hellish. Even the most long-suffering partner will object to life in an ancient caravan, and having to break the ice on the toothpaste tube in the depths of January.

Thirdly, don't lose your sense of humour. And finally, and most important of all, resolve from the outset that when and if things go wrong, you won't blame the other person.

Chapter 7: Choices in design

Choosing the design of your house is absolutely fundamental to self build: for many people, this is really what it's all about. But what should you choose?

Timber frame suppliers sometimes offer only their own standard ranges, and don't do one-offs; but even these standard designs are extremely flexible, and can be customised to some extent.

Other companies may not have a portfolio of their own at all, specialising purely in one-offs; and some will offer both standard designs and will also make timber frames to individual specification.

Many people choose their dream home simply by looking through the brochures and picking out what they like.

Some of the larger companies will have showhouse complexes; others will take you to see houses which are already built; self build exhibitions are an excellent way to meet lots of different suppliers and find out about their services and designs.

It's important to realise that even a small standard design offers enormous flexibility. Even if you were to say 'That one, please', the chances are that your finished product would look quite unlike anyone else's version. The choice of materials, especially brick and tiles, makes a big difference.

Most people vary their standard designs, depending on their own requirements and the orientation of the plot. A very common variation is to 'hand' the internal layout, ie swap rooms over from left to right, or from right to left. You might want a cathedral style hall, even if it meant losing a bedroom. Equally, you might consider an enormous hall and landing a waste of space, and want to incorporate an extra room.

In many cases, CAD systems (Computer Aided Design) can be brought into play: clients can literally sit with company designers, altering layouts and design features, and seeing the results on screen. CAD systems are being used increasingly by the bigger timber frame companies. In the most advanced systems, you can get special programmes, which enable you to switch on a computer, and be 'walked' through a 'book' of house designs. See one you like, and you can continue your 'walk' through each room of the house, and right round the outside. You can tweak each design as you please. Or if you want to start from scratch, you can design your own house on computer, see it take shape, and alter it as you go along.

Your own design

Every timber frame manufacturer has at some time or other been approached by a self builder with a gleam in their eye, and a drawing on the back of an envelope. Some companies specialise in converting these sketches into architectural plans.

You could also go to an independent architect and again, most timber frame companies will be happy to construct from an architect's designs.

What you do need to beware of is finding what looks like a perfect house plan, perhaps in a book of plans or in a company brochure, and then asking another company to handle it for you. Be careful! You are breaching copyright here, and you could be prosecuted.

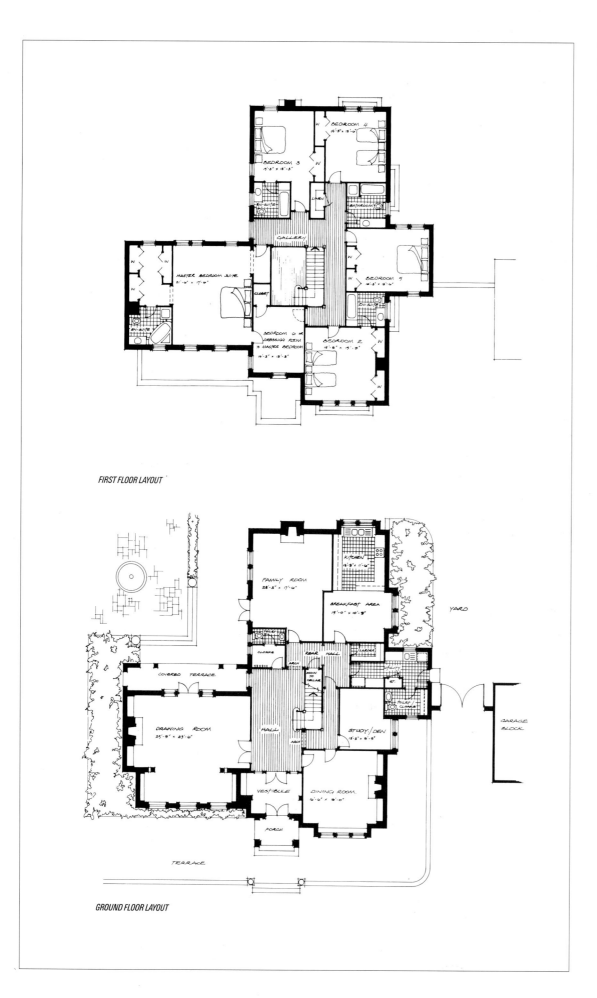

FIRST FLOOR LAYOUT

GROUND FLOOR LAYOUT

The Sunningdale, by Oliver Homes, is one of the largest homes from their prestige range. With a floor area of over 5,000 square feet, it would cost between £250,000 and £275,000 to build, assuming an overall high standard of fixtures and fittings (1993 price, excluding plot). With up to six bedrooms, two ground floor cloakrooms, and provision for a cellar, this is a classic design. The drawing room features period columns.

Modelled on a 16th century Japanese design, the distinctive Haiku house is manufactured in America and now available in this country. Of pole construction (the poles, not the walls, bear the load of the house), these elevated houses have verandas all the way round and huge, flexible open-plan living areas.

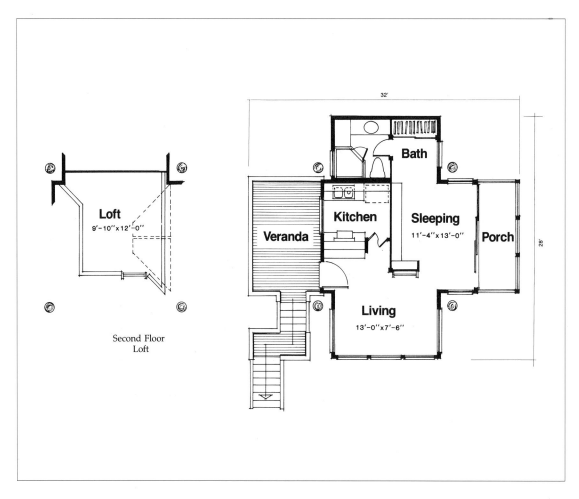

Loft
9'-10''x12'-0''

Second Floor
Loft

Bath

Kitchen

Veranda

Sleeping
11'-4''x13'-0''

Porch

Living
13'-0''x7'-6''

32'

28'

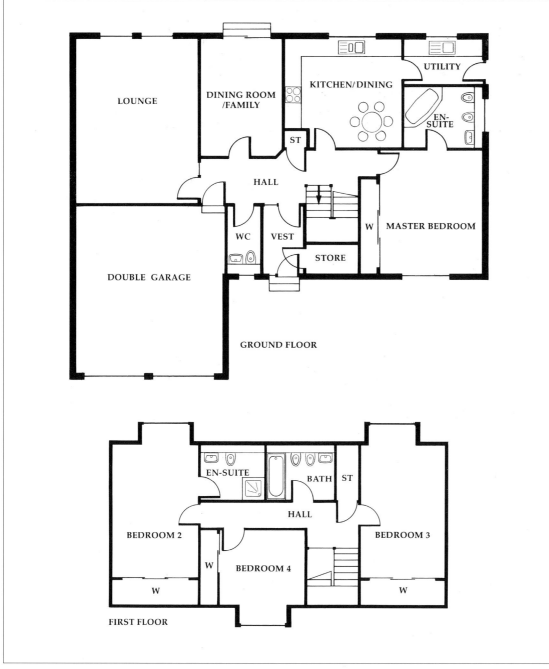

The Montpelier by the
Scottish company, Robertson
Homes, is a chalet-style
house. Excluding the garage,
it offers 1,989 square feet of
living space. The design
would be a very good choice
for a family needing virtually
self-contained granny or
teenage accommodation,
with its bedroom and
bathroom suite on the ground
floor. The double garage
also has obvious potential
for conversion into extra
living space.

The Kynance from
Cornish-based company Frame
Homes is the perfect choice
for anyone whose plot has
a commanding view.
The bedrooms are on the
ground floor and the
reception rooms on the upper
floor to take full advantage
of the site.

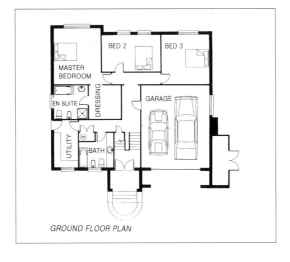

GROUND FLOOR PLAN

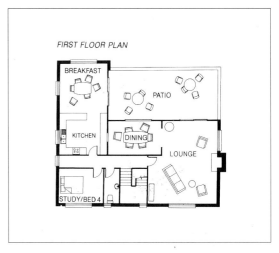

FIRST FLOOR PLAN

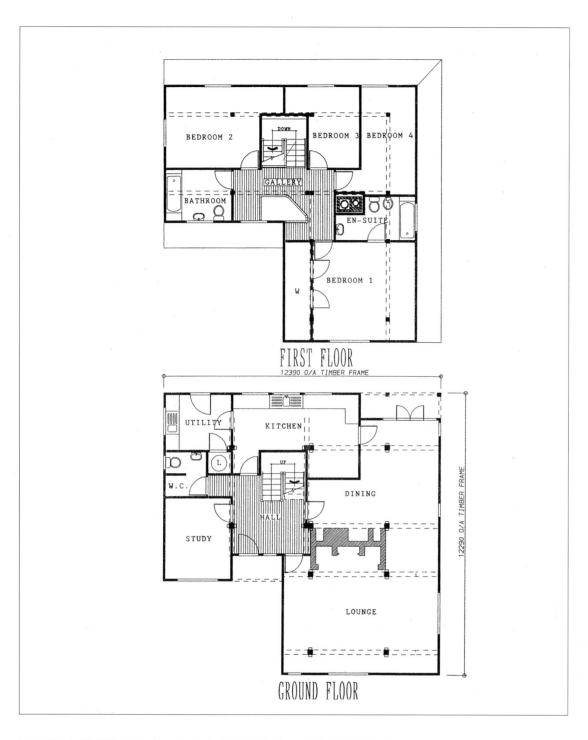

BEDROOM 2

DOWN

BEDROOM 3 BEDROOM 4

GALLERY

BATHROOM

EN-SUITE

BEDROOM 1

W

FIRST FLOOR

12390 O/A TIMBER FRAME

UTILITY

KITCHEN

L

UP

W.C.

DINING

STUDY

HALL

LOUNGE

12290 O/A TIMBER FRAME

GROUND FLOOR

The Gransden E, with its exposed posts and beams, is from Potton's Heritage range. Its large hall and gallery area are important design features. The master bedroom and its ensuite are at a physical distance from the other bedrooms. (Copyright Potton 1980)

FRONT

REAR

A typical American home, imported by the Yorkshire-based firm Pacific Wood. The accent is on large, wide open spaces with living areas that flow into each other. The overall living area is 1,862 square feet, with plenty of room in the loft area. This design would make the most of a split level site.

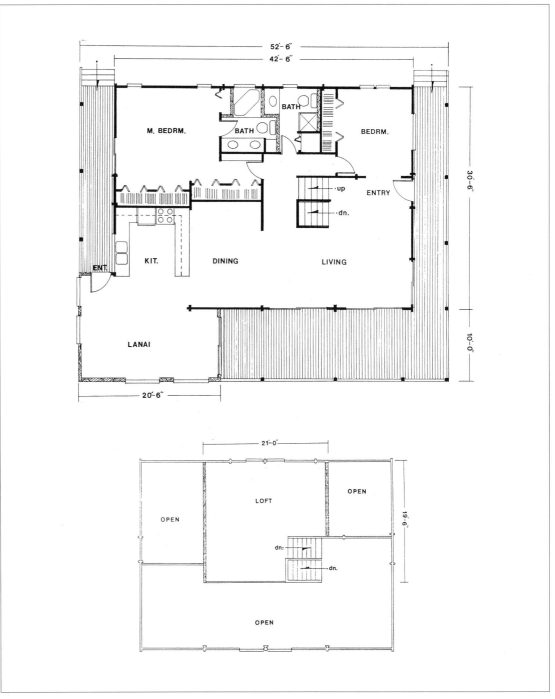

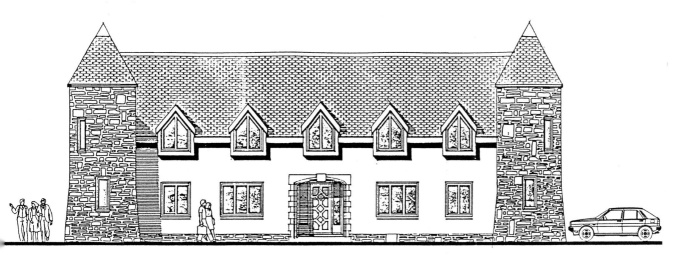

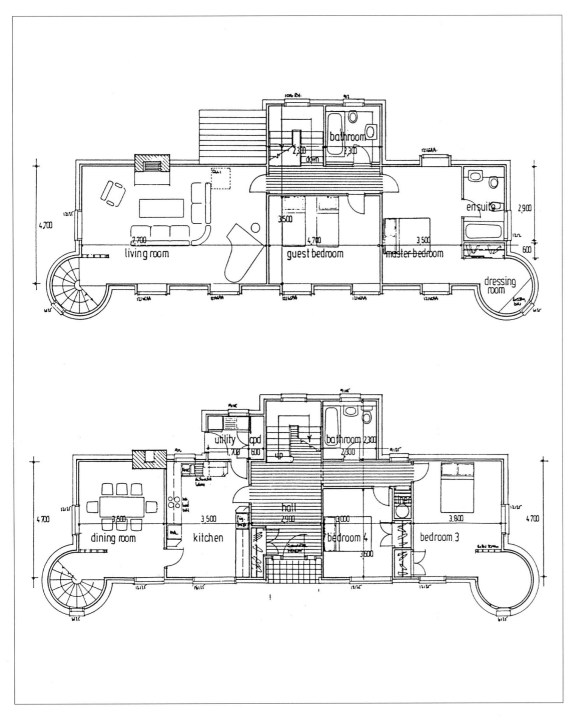

The Classic Chateau from
Border Design has trademark
round towers and a distinct
Gothic feel. A thoroughly
interesting and varied design,
it is suitable for a plot with
a wide frontage.

Neptune Cottage comes from Medina Gimson's much acclaimed Yeoman range. The external elevation packs in the interest, with its overhanging first floor.
As the internal plans show, accommodation can be flexible, producing three or four bedrooms.

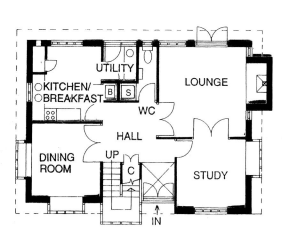

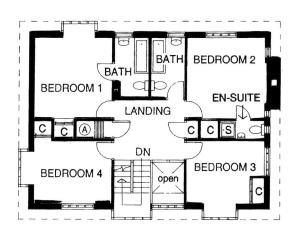

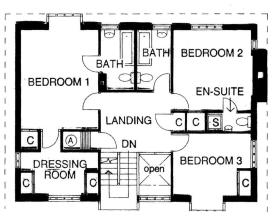

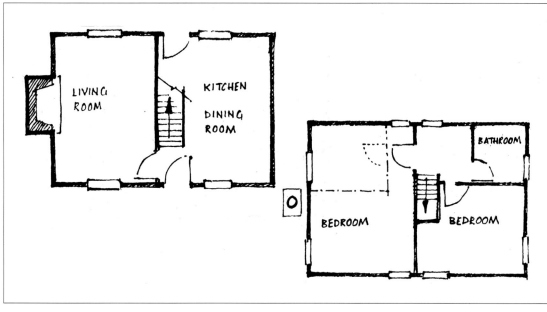

This tiny cottage has only 800 square feet of accommodation, but it is big enough for two or three bedrooms. Downstairs, just two large rooms are deceptively generous. Supplied by Border Oak, Monkland Cottage comes complete with inglenook fireplace, exposed oak beams, period doors, and casement windows. The roof is tiled here, but could equally be thatched.

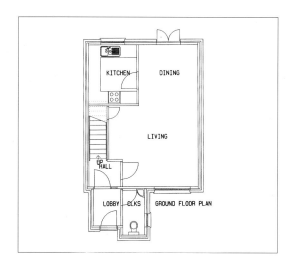

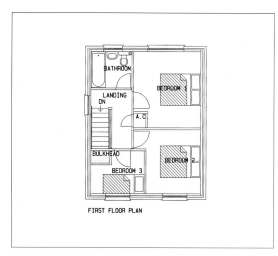

Smaller still! This tiny
702 square foot house
is by Isle of Wight-based
Moreys Manufacturing.
It has a frontage of just
18 feet, making it ideal for
a small infill plot.
It nevertheless packs
in three bedrooms.

Suiting the site

The site, quite as much as your taste, will dictate what your self build house will look like and how easily it can be built.

Sloping sites can be both difficult and rewarding. You may have to excavate the site thoroughly, so that a level base is obtained; but you could exploit it to have a home of different levels. One timber frame house, in a steeply sloping street in Henley-on-Thames, was built in an infill plot between two other houses. As if the slope were not difficult enough, there was a tree with a preservation order very close to the actual building site. It meant that the foundations had to be excavated very deeply, both to obtain a level base and to get beneath the tree roots. The deeper excavation meant that a useful basement could be incorporated.

A sloping site can be ideal if you have set your sights on a split level house, but this is where you need an architect to advise you on what can be achieved and how much it will cost.

Perhaps the most common site of all is an infill plot, usually taken from the side garden of a neighbouring house. This has several implications. First, it must fit in with its neighbours; the planning authority's chief concern is to see that a new house is in keeping with what is usually called the street scene.

Infill sites are usually long and narrow, so that your house design will have to reflect this shape. This sometimes calls for considerable ingenuity, and very likely, an integral garage if a garage cannot be fitted in at the side or at the front. Another important implication of an infill site is the need to maintain neighbours' privacy. Probably this will mean no large windows on the side elevations. In practice, a house on an infill plot is narrow and deep, with all main rooms looking straight out to the front or back, and bathrooms, cloakrooms and utility tucked into the sides.

In suiting your house design to your plot, you will have to take other things into consideration. A wooded plot is an example. Trees with preservation orders may heavily limit what you can do, and may dictate both the size and actual siting of your house. But of course, a site isn't just about limitations, but also about potential. In other words, make the most of the site you are working on and explore all its possibilities, taking advantage of the views and any interesting features.

As a general rule, it is very important for a self builder to develop the site in the right proportions. If you under-develop a site, for example by building a two-bedroomed bungalow on an acre, you are not going to be making the most of your plot, which means failing to maximise your asset. This might not matter to you, if a two bedroomed bungalow is all you need; but as an investment it is not ideal, as you would find when you came to sell.

Over-developing the plot, which means placing a huge house on a tiny plot, is just as bad. People expect big houses to have reasonable gardens.

Plot checklist

Is your site going to be easy or difficult to develop? Here are ten design considerations.

1. Does the site slope significantly? If so, can you make the slope work for you?

2. Is the site the right shape for what you want to build on it?

3. Are there immediate neighbours, so that the design of your home will need to take their need for privacy into consideration?

4. Is the plot heavily wooded?

5. Are there trees on the site which are protected by Tree Preservation Orders?

6. Will you be able to utilise a south-facing orientation, for example by placing all your main rooms to face south?

7. Is there room for a garage, or will you have to make some compromises here (eg opt for an integral garage because there is no space for a detached one)?

8. Is there a view you would like to maximise – or one you would prefer to 'lose'?

9. Is the plot the appropriate size, ie not too big and not too small, for the home you have in mind?

10. If you have your heart set on something special – like a split level design, a basement, or a balcony – will this be out of keeping on this particular plot?

House or bungalow?

Britain has an enduring affection for the bungalow. How planners view bungalows is likely to be dependent on both their immediate surroundings and the case you are able to make for building a single storey home. Generally speaking, planners do not like to see a run of two-storey homes interrupted by a bungalow in their midst; this works the other way too – planners will not want a sea of bungalows dwarfed by a towering new house!

Bungalows can be difficult to get right; too easily, they can look as though they are 'all roof', and in Scotland, there have been particular criticisms about the design of timber frame bungalows in the countryside for this reason. Bungalows can be stunning, but they need imaginative design, and they are usually at their most successful if given different roof levels and a bold, open layout.

Although bungalows are often regarded as small houses, they take up significantly more ground area than houses. It follows that they also have more roof area. In a large bungalow, the sheer size of this roof area can be very problematic, and the design should ensure that there is an interesting and varied pitch.

Because bungalows take up more ground area than houses, it's imperative they have a roomy enough plot. Bungalows look best with space around them.

Bungalows are relatively expensive to build, compared with houses; that is because it is cheaper to build on two floors, than to do extra foundation work and pay for the larger roof. On the other hand, a bungalow uses its internal space more effectively than a house, because there is no need for a large hall, landing or stairwell.

Per square foot, a bungalow will cost more to build than a house; however, more of that square footage will be habitable space.

Style features

In theory, self builders have more scope in terms of design features than anyone else. In practice, it is noticeable how many self builders have a love of classic quality, as reflected in the majority of standard designs offered by timber frame suppliers. Comparatively few self builders pick futuristic designs, or choose to boldly go where no one else has been.

This innate conservatism is probably just as well, since planners prefer to play safe. Above all, they like new houses to be 'in keeping'.

The self builder does well, therefore, to look at properties not only in the immediate surrounding area, but also over a wider region. In Kent, for instance, they like tilehanging; in Essex, they prefer

weatherboarding. If you are building in the Cotswolds or parts of Somerset or Yorkshire, the planners may insist that you clad your house in stone, whilst in Cornwall and Scotland, render is the norm.

If you are building in a conservation area, in an area of outstanding natural beauty, of special landscape value, or any other designated planning zone, watch it! The planners will want to ensure that the design of your house fits in with its surroundings, and will dictate the building materials you may use. It would be as well to use a local architect with a track record of success with the planners, or to approach the planners themselves for preliminary advice on the kind of design they would find acceptable.

This may mean clay tiles or slates, not a concrete roof. It may mean stone instead of brick. The cost and practical implications should be looked at carefully. If stone is a requirement, discuss this with your timber frame suppliers before you buy, and not after. Most timber frames are designed to have four inches of brick on them, not eight inches of stone!

It's fair to say that most of the standard designs now offered by timber frame suppliers really are very enticing: the big names have their standard ranges nicely worked out.

Planning authorities can be more circumspect with American or Scandinavian style houses, which is why most of the companies concerned are now at pains to offer traditional British looking houses.

That is, they look traditionally British on the outside, and appropriately American or Scandinavian on the inside, with a large, open lay-out, plenty of use of split levels, and generous use of wood.

Function of design

Never forget when trying to decide on how your dream home should look, that design should also have a function.

It is perfectly possible to design for energy efficiency, and therefore economy. If this is something that particularly interests you, it would be worth consulting an architect with a particular interest in 'green' buildings.

The following features will often be included in 'green' buildings:

Windows of most rooms would face south, or be oriented within 30 degrees of south

Conservatories would be on a southern, not northern, elevation

All **external entrances** would be protected from the weather with draughtproof lobbies or porches

Internal layout

The planners are not, you will be pleased to hear, interested in the internal layout of your house. The Building Regulations people are also largely indifferent, although you need to ensure that you do not have a loo leading straight off your kitchen.

Otherwise, do what you please, although if you ever want to sell your house, it would be as well to pay attention to current tastes. Estate agents say that the features most likely to sell a house quickly include: a downstairs cloakroom, separate utility room, and one en suite bathroom as well as a family bathroom upstairs.

Generally speaking, tastes are shifting towards a third bathroom (or ensuite shower room) to serve a guest bedroom; galleried landings overlooking large halls; and it is very difficult to see the small kitchen making a comeback. But of course the main thing if you are self building is to suit the needs of yourself and your family. Another important consideration for most families is orientation: to have main rooms looking south or over the garden (preferably both).

Layout checklist

Everyone enjoys playing around with designs for their own dream house, and you may not be able to resist getting some squared paper and drawing up some floor layouts. Even if you don't go this far, you should still spend time thinking through every possible element of the internal design. You will then be able to give your architect or designer a very detailed brief of what you want.

1. Lounge. Note down the features you would like to see in this. For instance, should it have an open fireplace? Would you like a double or triple aspect? How large would you like this room?

2. Dining room. Do you want this separate, or to open out from the lounge via double doors?

3. Kitchen. Classically found at the back of the house. Choices are to combine this with a breakfast room; or to have an adjoining breakfast room.

4. Utility. This usually leads off the kitchen and has direct access to outside. But you could also, or instead, consider a laundry room.

5. Laundry room. This could work very well upstairs, and incorporate airing and ironing facilities.

6. Family room. Usually placed close to the kitchen.

7. Study. Generally the smallest room in the house if it's downstairs. In a larger house, a room designated as a bedroom could be used as the study (note: be careful on any planning application to call a study a study, and not an office, in case it's thought you are trying to set up a business from home).

8. Downstairs cloakroom. In bigger houses, consider having two - a guest cloakroom, and one just off the utility room, where family can come straight in from outside and not have to trail through the house.

9. Hall. Modern tastes like big halls. Be careful, however, not to overdo the size, or it throws the proportions out.

10. Stairs. Classic designs, rather than open plan treads, are popular.

11. Landings. Again, a large landing has regained popularity. Some landings are even designed as 'wasted space', to be used for television watching, sewing, hobbies and so on. Scandinavian houses are a prime example.

12. Bedrooms. How many, how big, and how many should have ensuite bathrooms? Could two bedrooms share one bathroom? Plan all bedrooms with storage in mind.

13. The master suite. In a large house could have its own sitting room, dressing room and bathroom.

Size of house

Timber frame lends itself to the smallest bungalow as well as to mansions. I know of 950 square foot bungalows in timber frame, and of at least one house with more than 5,000 square feet of habitable living space.

Between these two extremes is the size of house most of us live in!

As a general rule of thumb, around 1,000 square feet is bungalow-size; around 1,300 square feet is a three-bedroomed house; a good family sized house is between 1,600 square feet and 2,000. Most of the standard ranges offer 'top' sizes of about 3,000 square feet which, in the most general terms, would offer you five bedrooms and two or three bathrooms, and at least three reception rooms.

As another rule of thumb, the bigger you build, the less expensive it is to achieve in terms of cost per square foot.

A final word about square feet: as has already been said, this is the internal, habitable space. One or two suppliers interpret it to mean the overall substance of the house, so make sure you are talking about the same thing. Square footage does not include a garage, or if it does, should make it clear, eg 1,800 square feet including garage.

If you are specifying, however, do make absolutely clear what you want in the way of true square footage, and express it thus: 1,400 square feet plus 400 square feet double garage. When costing your house in terms of square feet, don't include the garage. Unless you have installed fitted carpet and central heating in it, it won't have cost nearly as much per square foot as your home.

Garages, landscaping and outbuildings

Do consider these in relation to your house. The first two should form part of the project; they can be part of the same planning application and planners will want to approve your landscaping plans anyway. A garage can be part of the original planning application (and the planners may insist that it is), or could form a separate application of its own.

Planners sometimes have curious ideas about landscaping: we weren't allowed to plant a weeping willow tree, on the grounds that it wasn't indigenous to the landscape (they obviously didn't see the others in the village!). However, don't let this worry you since once the house is finished and the planners have departed, you can plant whatever you like.

What planners - and of course you - want to see is a harmonious plan, so that garage, house and landscaping all complement each other.

Garages are a subject on their own, but for the purposes of this book, you need to ask yourself whether yours should be timber frame or brick and block. If timber frame, then there is the obvious advantage of speed of erection. It can be designed to match your house, and clad in the same way. However, most cars would not require the famous energy efficient insulation that makes a timber frame home such an attractive bet.

Most of the big timber frame suppliers have standard garage ranges; in an ideal world, you would probably have your garage built at the same time as your house. If it is on the same planning application, it would count as the same project, and you could reclaim VAT on it as well.

You can also reclaim VAT on landscaping such as terraces, patios and gravel for your drive.

Example of working drawings.

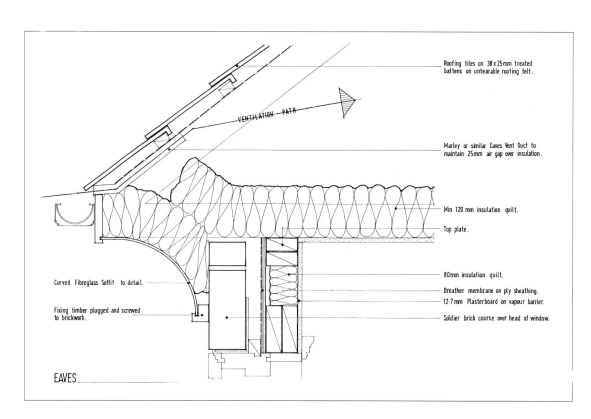

Roofing tiles on 38 x 25mm treated battens on untearable roofing felt.

VENTILATION PATH

Marley or similar Eaves Vent Duct to maintain 25mm air gap over insulation.

Min 120 mm insulation quilt.

Top plate.

80mm insulation quilt.

Breather membrane on ply sheathing.

12·7 mm Plasterboard on vapour barrier.

Soldier brick course over head of window.

Curved Fibreglass Soffit to detail.

Fixing timber plugged and screwed to brickwork.

EAVES

One word more about garages: many will be built with room to spare under a pitched roof. People often like to have this boarded, so that the room can be used for teenage hobbies or a studio. The planners would probably approve this. They would not, however, approve of a garage loft being turned into actual living space; if they were to find out that you were doing this, they might well initiate enforcement action to make you stop.

You don't need planning approval for garden sheds, greenhouses, or most outbuildings unless they are large or unless you intend to run a business from them.

> **In general design terms, you should:**
>
> • **Ensure your garage has a design that goes with your house. In particular, the pitch of the garage roof should reflect that of your house. Materials should also be the same.**
>
> • **Landscape in proportion to your house. The larger the house, the larger the hard areas (ie, patio, pathways, etc) around it will need to be.**

Working drawings

These will come as part and parcel of your timber frame, and there will be a working drawing to cover every single phase of construction and every single part of your new home.

If you are managing your own build, one of your roles is to ensure that your sub-contractors are actually working to those working drawings. If you are not sure, ask. Where your sub-contractors are unsure as to what is meant, encourage them to speak to your architect for interpretation, or to ring the timber frame supplier for advice.

Problems can arise when you have two sets of drawings. For example, if an engineer has designed your foundations, check that the dimensions are exactly the same as those on the working drawings that have come from the timber frame suppliers. If there's any discrepancy, don't let work start or continue until you have identified exactly which drawing should be worked to. If any doubt still remains, you could ask both the timber frame supplier and the engineer to check both sets of drawings against one another.

Problems can also arise when sub-contractors misinterpret the working drawings, or say they know a better way to do it! If you are managing your build and suspect this is the case, halt work and call in help. When my own build was going ahead, I realised that the outer brick cladding was being put up without fire stops being put in first. So keep on top of those drawings, try to understand them, and make sure you see your sub-contractors actually looking at them.

Example of working drawings.

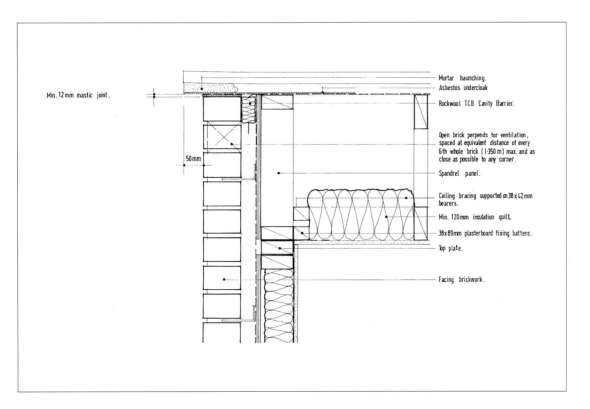

Min. 12 mm mastic joint.

50 mm

Mortar haunching.
Asbestos undercloak
Rockwool TCB Cavity Barrier.
Open brick perpends for ventilation, spaced at equivalent distance of every 6th whole brick (1·350 m) max. and as close as possible to any corner.
Spandrel panel.
Ceiling bracing supported on 38 x 42 mm bearers.
Min. 120 mm insulation quilt.
38 x 89 mm plasterboard fixing battens.
Top plate.
Facing brickwork.

Chapter 8: Who's in charge?

The term 'self builder' is a confusing one. People tend to believe it means actually building the house yourself. When you introduce yourself as a self builder, they'll gulp and fall back in admiration, ready to believe that you have knocked up a house in your spare time, alternating hod carrying with your full time job in an office.

It's nice to bask in the adulation, but the reality is likely to be quite different. Self build, for the most part, is about managing, not necessarily about DIY at all. Of course, it does not have to exclude DIY; it's just that it's not compulsory.

But what will self build actually mean to you? It could mean:

1. Organising the whole thing from start to finish – finding the plot, getting planning permission, organising finance, and so on. You will now physically build a fair bit of the house yourself, using your own skills and labour, with some help from sub-contractors. In football terms, that makes you the player/manager.

2. You've organised everything so far, ie until the actual building starts. Now you are going to be your own site foreman. You'll be in charge of the building of your own house, but you don't expect to do much – or perhaps any – of the actual work yourself. This makes you, again using the football analogy, the 'manager'.

3. Again, you've organised the lot so far. Now you're ready to start building. You are going to have the actual structure of the house built and managed by an NHBC builder, through from foundations to when it has its roof on. Then, you will take over managing the rest of the build – mostly, this means handling what are called the 'finishing trades', the electrical, plumbing, heating, joinery and decorating.

4. You have organised the land, finance, planning and design angles as above. The house is now going to be built by various builders and sub-contractors chosen and managed for you by an architect, consultant or some other property professional.

5. You have organised buying the land, arranged the finance and achieved planning permission. You have also chosen the design of your house. Now the whole house is going to be built and managed, as one complete job, by a builder.

6. Yours is the line of least resistance! Really, all you're interested in is choosing the design of your dream house, and then walking through the door when it's built. A full service from a package company, please!

These are the main options. All are forms of self build, and all have advantages. Let's look at each in turn:

1. The DIY builder

The immediate advantage of being a player/manager is that you will make the biggest savings available to self builders. The irony is that these savings may not be as cost-effective as you think.

This is because physically building your own house is a huge commitment. If you have to give up work to do it, the savings you make on labour will have to be set against your own salary losses. If you don't give up work, you will have only evenings and weekends to build the house, and so the building period could lengthen.

If this means having to pay rent or interest charges over a longer period of time, then building your house cheaply could actually cost you money.

Do-it-yourself building could be what your particular dream is all about, in which case, good luck. But savings made by self building invariably come from good management, not from contributing your own labour.

> **If you are contemplating DIY self building, go ahead if:**
>
> - **You are certain of doing a really good job to professional standards, and you can get your work guaranteed**
> - **You never lose sight of the fact that it is your good management, rather than your physical input, that will be cost-effective**
> - **The savings you make by building your house yourself are not offset by earnings losses**
> - **You will be able to build on a cost-effective time scale**

2. Your own site foreman/manager

You might not so much as pick up a brick, but by managing your build efficiently, you stand to save considerable sums of money and to make your self build an economic success.

This management role is the one that more and more self builders want. They take the view that they are neither bricklayers nor carpenters, and that it is better to maintain their usual incomes while letting the professionals get on with the job. Managing the build efficiently is still likely to be very consuming of time and energy, but the feeling of achievement is terrific. It is also a role that husbands and wives can share.

3. NHBC builder to roof stage

Some people believe this combines the best of all worlds, because it enables you to get the NHBC Buildmark for the foundations, walls and roof, while maintaining a good level of participation. When the house has reached weatherproof stage, you can then take over, and sub-contract all the other work.

This option is easy to arrange if you are buying a brick and block package, where one builder could easily construct the whole house to weathertight stage. With a timber frame, the complication could be the need for a specialist erection team as well as a builder. Appointing an architect to supervise the whole build and give progress certificates is recommended.

4. Getting your build professionally managed

Here, your choices include an architect, surveyor, a builder, or simply a consultant who has made self build his speciality. This is the method for you if you don't want to manage the build yourself, but would prefer a wider choice of materials and sub-contractors. Professional managers can also do a lot more than simply manage your build: for instance, they can handle plot purchase, planning permission, and Building Regulations. Getting your build wholly managed for you can be an expensive way of self building, although there's no doubt that professionals can save you money through their sheer expertise. However, the expertise could cost you anything up to 10 per cent of the finished cost of your home.

5. One contractor builds your whole house

This is the option for you if you lack time, energy and confidence. But please don't consider using a non-NHBC or non-Foundation 15 registered builder, and make it clear from the outset that you want a Buildmark guarantee, or Foundation 15 warranty.

It is not a method for anyone wanting active day-to-day participation in the management of the build; nevertheless, as an employer, you should still be making decisions and will feel fully involved.

The advantage of this method is that you will not be charged VAT. In theory, using one builder is hassle-free; in practice, one often hears otherwise. One drawback is that your chosen builder may be better and more competitively priced in some areas of work, than in others. The other is that some of the money you hand over to him will be his profit. Again, employing a professional to supervise the work and administer the building contract is advisable.

6. Full service

This is when the timber frame supplier accomplishes the whole build for you. A few companies insist on it, on the basis that they want each of their houses to be properly built and finished. Most companies, however, have flexible packages of supply and service, which can be tailored to individual customers.

If you want a full service, you will have to pay for it. On the other hand, when things go wrong, it won't be your problem. In fact, you might not even know about it. It's not the method for you if you want to feel fully involved; it's perfect for you if you want a full turn key job.

Kit companies

As mentioned above virtually all the companies offer flexible packages which range from design and supply, right through to full build.

One popular option is to buy the frame and have it erected. Companies may have their own erection teams, or use regular sub-contractors. There is no reason why you should not find your own erection team, or at least get an independent quote to compare with the company price.

A local carpenter may seem enthusiastic, but actual experience with timber frame is what you want. Let him practise somewhere else!

Another popular package is to buy the frame, have it erected and then have the kit supplier's men do both first and second joinery fixes. Again, it's worth getting a competitive quote.

Whatever package you choose, make some checks first:

- Ask to be put in touch with previous clients. Talk to them about the service they received, and about how any problems were recognised and dealt with.

- Ask if the company pays routine visits to check key stages of the build. If this question receives a hollow laugh from the sales team, hesitate before you sign your cheque. Some companies do include a series of routine visits in their service. All of them should. This is, after all, a huge investment for you and you deserve a little hand-holding.

Complete packages

If you want a complete package from your supplier, it's obviously important to get the best possible deal, and your contract should be watertight. Involve your solicitor. In particular:

- Ask the company to be specific about its timescale. Some companies will penalise themselves for lateness by handing money back to the client.

- Your finished house should be fully guaranteed against defects. Check this out: will you have an NHBC or Foundation 15 warranty? Will the suppliers themselves guarantee the house against defects, or at least promise to put right any that might occur following the build?

- Make clear the terms of your snag list – those irritating snags only identified after you've actually moved in and are living with them, such as leaking washers, a faulty window catch, a noisy boiler, and so on. Agree before you sign the contract that you will both draw up a snag list, to be sorted out at no expense to you within six months. It would be normal to withhold a small amount of money until this period was up. Agree an actual sum or percentage – probably around two and a half per cent of the total contract.

Although a complete package spares you the stress of management, it should not eliminate you from the pleasures of self building. Make clear that you will want to visit your build regularly, will wish to feel involved, and will want to make decisions and suggestions.

Architects

In the context of managing your build, as opposed to simply designing your house, an architect could have an important role to play.

He or she will visit your build at key stages and give progress certificates. On receipt of these, your lender will release the next stage of payment. On completion, the architect will certify the whole build. This certification is your guarantee, backed by the architect's own professional indemnity insurance, that your house has been soundly constructed. Should problems arise subsequently, your redress is against the architect, whose professional insurance has been taken out against exactly this possibility.

Before employing an architect as your manager, you should:

- Check that your lender will be happy with architect's certificates to guarantee your build. One or two building societies may not accept them; the majority will.

- Check with your architect that he or she has professional indemnity insurance.

A good arrangement is to appoint an architect to see your build through in a pre-arranged number of visits both to supervise progress and issue progress certificates. This is not the same thing as asking him to manage the entire build on your behalf; it is simply using his or her expertise as back-up. Anything between five and ten visits could be agreed.

Used in this way, an architect can be invaluable in finding solutions, checking work, and advising you whether to withhold payment or ask for improvements.

If you do want to employ an architect to design and then handle your entire build for you, then this is a very different ball game. The RIBA's leaflets will tell you what is involved. Your architect will design your home, get planning permission, help you choose your builders, draw up detailed working drawings, tell you when to pay the builder, and manage the whole of the actual build, and of course, certify it.

This level of service suits some people, but not all. The RIBA urges clients: *"Take an interest in the construction but never give instructions direct to the builder – only through your architect."* It also counsels against changing your mind once building work has started, as this might cost you money. The point is that when you employ an architect at this level, you are appointing him to be boss. If you prefer to be the one in control, you would do better to sort out a different kind of working relationship.

Management companies and consultants

Some companies and consultants will make all the arrangements for you, including manufacture, supply, erect, build and complete finish of your build.

They may or may not be professionally qualified in some way – as chartered surveyors, for instance. Or they may have a background of building, or having managed their own build successfully, now feel it's a sphere they can go into professionally. Find out and make sure that they are insured.

These consultant companies and individuals regularly advertise, usually offering partial or complete project management. Many can also arrange finance, and will handle planning. Some of these consultants also have a specific relationship with an individual timber frame manufacturer, so claim experience with those particular products.

If you want to employ a project manager, think hard. It is also worth your while to:

- **Draw up a legal contract for their services**
- **Make sure they have real hands-on experience in building with timber frame**
- **Ask to see examples of their work, and talk to previous clients**
- **If they offer to arrange finance and planning, hesitate before going any further. What are they really offering? They may be 'tied' agents, working on commission to arrange you a loan or insurance. As for planning, this can be a sensitive subject: real professional experience and/or local knowledge are called for.**
- **Check that your build will be covered by a professional guarantee.**

Guarantees

Getting your build guaranteed is essential. If you have a lender, it will be a requirement, and the lender may stipulate who is to do the guaranteeing, nominating Foundation 15, the NHBC, for

instance, or an architect with professional indemnity insurance. These mean that you can bring a claim in the event of a subsequent structural defect. To get your house guaranteed, it will need to be regularly inspected during the course of its build, so that the guarantor knows that the construction is up to standard.

All lenders will accept NHBC and Foundation 15 guarantees. NHBC is a structural guarantee that lasts ten years; Foundation 15 guarantees houses for up to 15. The two systems differ in that the NHBC means having to use a builder registered with the NHBC. The Foundation 15 scheme is better geared to self builders, because it does not insist on using a particular builder. Once you have registered your build with the scheme, it gives you the freedom to manage the whole thing yourself, using subcontractors as you wish and/or your own labour. All that matters is that the work comes up to the standard required by the Foundation 15 inspector.

If you do not want to manage the build yourself, but would still like the option of a longer warranty offered by Foundation15, then simply ensure that you use a Foundation 15 registered builder. To get an NHBC Buildmark warranty, only the builder (not the self builder) can apply: the cost depends on the final market value of your property.

Interestingly, the NHBC has just started a new pilot scheme for self builders, which gives their homes a full ten year structural cover. The scheme is currently only available in Northern Ireland and on the Isle of Man, and seems to be very similar to Foundation 15. Fees are reasonable, at £520 for a property that will be worth more than £100,000 on completion.

Virtually all lenders state they will be happy with an architect's certification; another possibility is to use a chartered surveyor, or maybe a structural engineer.

If you need no lender to finance your self build, you may want to dispense with guarantees. The advice is simple. Don't!

You wouldn't buy a new house without a guarantee, so please don't build one. If you did, you could well find it unsaleable, because building societies would take a very sniffy view of a new house built without a structural guarantee. You may think you are building for life, will never sell, and that therefore this doesn't apply to you. Think again. Life changes in mysterious and unexpected ways, and it is wise to be prepared for anything.

Chapter 9: You've been framed!

As explained at the beginning of the book, there are several different types of timber frame, each providing a different form of structure.

Platform frame

The most commonly used type of timber frame is the platform frame method which uses wall panels. Starting at the centre and working our way outwards, this is what you find.

First, there is the structural framework. This is a series of verticals and horizontals in stress graded softwood timber. When one talks about studs or studwork, this is what is meant. Studs are usually four inches thick, sometimes five or six inches. The thicker the studwork, the more insulation can be used.

1. This framework is strengthened by sheets, about three eighths of an inch thick, of plywood or fibre building boards, known as the sheathing. This provides enormous stiffness to withstand lateral loads. The sheathing board is nailed on to the timber studwork at calculated centres. Factory produced lintels are incorporated to take care of doors and windows.

2. When your timber frame is delivered on site, you will see that the framework is in the form of wall panels made up of the structural framework with the sheathing board already attached.

Also usually attached is the breather membrane, a waterproof cover on the sheathing board, which keeps rain out of the structure during construction and allows the wall to breathe. A breather membrane is not always needed, if an impregnated softwood fibre building board is used.

3. Beyond the breather membrane is a two inch (50mm) cavity, which keeps the outer cladding separate from the inner structure, and prevents rain from penetrating the inside.

This cavity should never be filled. Wall ties do cross it, connecting the inner timber frame to the outer cladding - this is perfectly acceptable.

4. Beyond the cavity is the cladding of your choice – brick, stone, weatherboarding or a rendered finish.

Going back to the structural framework and working our way inside this time, this is what we find:

1. Inside the sheathing board is the insulation material. It is non-combustible and its thickness varies according to specification. It is usually between four and six inches.

2. The insulation is held in place by the vapour check. The vapour check is either a separate polythene sheet, normally 500g thick, or it may be an alternative material which is part of the plasterboard lining. The vapour check is there to stop condensation produced inside your finished home getting into the timber frame.

3. Finally, the plasterboard lining: this gives internal walls and ceilings a smooth, dry surface which is ready for decorating. Gypsum plasterboard has good fire resistance. The plasterboard sometimes has structural significance.

The internal walls of a timber framed house are factory produced framed panels. Sometimes, if extra stiffness is required, they have sheathing board applied. Just as with brick and block constructions, some of the internal walls of a timber frame house may be load bearing. Where necessary, additional vertical studs are incorporated to carry the load to the foundations.

The upper floors consist of timber joists, supported by the structural timber frame. The floor itself is generally tongued and grooved plywood, chipboard or softwood boarding.

The roof structure is usually of trussed rafters – a modern, lightweight, prefabricated construction. Some timber frame manufacturers offer an attic roof construction. This has the advantage that if you want to extend into your loft, you can. A trussed rafter construction generally means that there is no usable room in a loft, other than for storage.

Some Scandinavian houses make a point of using loft space for - wait for it - drying clothes. This isn't as daft as it sounds, since thanks to modern Building Regulations, lofts are very well ventilated these days.

Post and beam

Some manufacturers also offer, or specialise in post and beam timber frames. Execution varies considerably, and may combine the two systems – post and beam and wall panels.

The Alberta, from Maple Leaf Homes, was featured at the 1993 Ideal Home Exhibition. It is a fine example of a high-tech house hidden behind a traditional facade.

Another showhouse from the 1993 Ideal Home Exhibition was the Hudson, also from Maple Leaf Homes. Like the Alberta, it is a very large house with a ground floor area of about 3,000 square feet.

The well-known Heritage range from Potton features the post and beam principle. Here, the main structure is an 'aisle frame' built in timber. Load bearing is on the cantilever principle – in other words, it is spread out from within, leaving the external walls relatively lightly loaded.

The Heritage range leaves many of the load bearing beams attractively exposed. The main frames and end walls enclose a series of square spaces extended on each side by the 'aisles'. These squares can be joined and linked to make a progressively larger house. The external walls of a Heritage house are finished and packed with insulation in just the same way as in the platform frame panel system.

Vernacular

The post and beam, or post and truss, system of timber frame is also practised by Lindal Cedar Homes, the American company, and Border Oak, the (very!) British one, and a tiny handful of others (usually individual specialists) devoted to traditional, vernacular architecture.

Post and beam is usually claimed – with some historical justification – to be the 'real' form of timber frame. The frame resembles a skeleton of timbers, with the posts and beams supporting the roof's weight, instead of the walls. Like the panel system, however, construction is pre-fabricated off-site.

Border Oak uses substantial oak frames from home-grown trees, not imported softwood. Their oak framed houses are divided into modules, called 'bays', by construction – in the old days, they would talk about a house having so many bays, just as today, we refer to a house having so many bedrooms. The frame consists of full height corner posts and shorter ground floor studs placed in the soleplate.

These are held in place by the girding rail, which as the name suggests is a rail that girds the entire perimeter of the building at first floor level, rather like a belt. Huge trusses and beams are lifted into position, and braces are used to stiffen up the whole building and add visual interest.

Border Oak's whole spirit of endeavour is to be as authentic and as faithful to the original as possible, and so Elizabethan carpentry methods are used, including dovetail jointing and seasoned oak pegs – no nails or glue! The insulation is however contemporary, and also quite different

from that used in panelled systems. Thermal infill panels (U value 0.275) are fitted into position, in between the timbers. These panels are filled with Styrofoam and rendered externally with oatmeal or honey coloured finish.

The roof construction also tends to be different. For instance, Border Oak's Barleymow Farmhouse has attic trusses, providing a useful 34 by 10 foot room.

Solid timber

Solid timber houses, sometimes known as 'log' houses, are a form of construction where there is no inner or outer frame, and no cavity. Nor is there a skeletal frame. Instead, solid timber walls interlock on top of foundations. The whole idea is to show off the beauty of the wood both inside and out – not to cover it with brick cladding on the outside, or plasterboard on the inside.

More and more examples of solid timber houses are coming into the UK, both from Scandinavia and the States where the wood is likely to be red cedar. Exact methods of construction and design do vary, but these homes are always claimed to be extremely strong and durable, and because they are solid timber, highly fire resistant.

Solid timber houses are highly energy efficient, with typically a one-and-a-half inch polystyrene core inside the wood walls. U-values are good at around 0.31. The method of construction is very quick, because each wall is erected ready-finished and insulated – no need for cladding and no need to decorate. They are usually also immensely strong structures. There are two currently being built on Scottish islands where wind gusts of up to 200mph are not unknown.

These houses frequently have basements – a standard requirement in America – and interesting interior design, making the most of the natural wood, and often incorporate split levels and open-plan areas. Sometimes, these timber houses combine a solid log construction on the ground floor with a framed upper floor.

In the past, reservations were expressed on three fronts: cost, planning approval (or disapproval!) and doubts about the ability to raise finance. Costs vary, but around £36 per square foot for a two-storey house supplied and erected seems average. Planners are becoming more sympathetic, and Building Regulations approval is not a problem. Finally, problems with raising finance in the normal

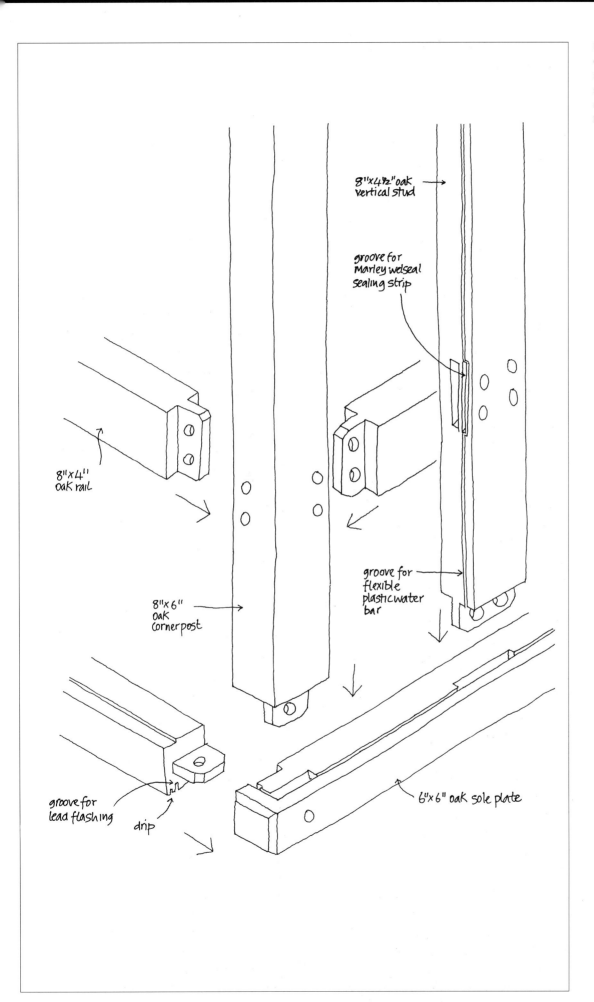

8"x4½" oak vertical stud

groove for Marley welseal sealing strip

8"x4" oak rail

8"x6" oak cornerpost

groove for flexible plastic water bar

groove for lead flashing

drip

6"x6" oak sole plate

Post and beam frames were originally held together with mortise and tenon joints - no nails! This method is still used by some manufacturers, including Border Oak.

Constructed from Lindal cedar, this solid timber house is the embodiment of the American dream home.

way are not likely to be encountered provided that the constructions have full Building Regulations approval – as, of course, all buildings must.

Pole houses

One form of timber frame worth mentioning is the Japanese style pole houses which, as the name suggests, are built on round poles.

Poles are said to be 18 per cent stronger than square posts. The poles are also claimed to be very versatile, and enable houses to be built up on stilts, whether on slopes, flood plains, riverside or other sites normally considered unbuildable. These houses are Japanese in style only – they're made from American timbers and crafted in Cornwall.

Beauty is in the eye of the beholder, but there are many people who find these Haiku houses

outstandingly beautiful. In the States, these pole-constructed houses have won a large number of awards.

Steel frame

It may sound odd to mention steel frame in a book about timber frame, but the principle of construction is the same. Only the material is different.

Indeed, some people believe that steel frame is the building system of tomorrow. It's very strong, well engineered and durable; it's flexible and as a method of construction it's very quick.

Possibly because of people's perceptions, steel framed housing has yet to take off. However, public perceptions change and possibly steel frame will indeed be the housing of the future.

The design for this unusual Haiku house is Japanese-inspired and is based around solid round poles.

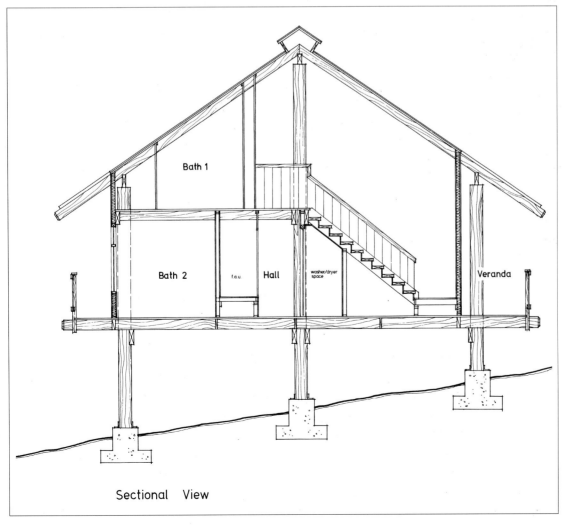

Bath 1

Bath 2   f.a.u.   Hall   washer/dryer space   Veranda

Sectional   View

Chapter 10: Managing your build

Right, you have your plot, your planning permission, your finance in place, and you are ready to start. It is now that you will discover the pleasures and pains of dealing with builders.

Your options are, in very simple terms:

- To put the whole, or major part of your build out to one contractor to both supply and fix

- To manage the build yourself, buying the materials yourself and using the labour of various specialist sub-contractors.

Hiring a builder, or sub-contractors, seems daunting to many self builders who may never have dealt with building tradesmen before. Just finding a builder seems difficult!

Without any doubt, the best way to find good contractors is by word of mouth. Ask friends, neighbours, and in the local pubs and shops. Ask for personal recommendations. Also look through Yellow Pages, and in the trades directories published in local newspapers. When considering taking on a contractor, ask to see examples of previous work or to talk to past customers. Membership of a professional body (for instance, the Federation of Master Builders, or the Electrical Contractors Association) is a helpful indication of good standards. In the case of the former, there is also a useful warranty scheme which gives you, amongst other things, a five year warranty on structural defects caused by faulty materials or workmanship, and a free conciliation service should you run into disputes.

Finding sub-contractors becomes easier as you go along, because one sub-contractor tends to recommend another.

Contracting a builder

If you are taking on just one builder (as opposed to a succession of sub-contractors) to supply and fix most or all of your build, you must be certain that you have picked the right one.

This is the time to call in professional advice. A lot of money (yours) is at stake, and you are going to need a contract. The most usual type is produced by an organisation called the Joint Contract Tribunal (JCT), which is made up of representatives of various professional bodies in the building industry,

and which has various types of contract to cover different schemes.

An architect or surveyor may recommend a JCT contract, or some other type of standard contract available from his or her professional body (eg the RIBA). Your professional adviser will have a good idea of what the job involves, how long it should take and how much it should cost. He – or she – will write the specification for the job, breaking it down into elements, invite quotes, and advise you which one to choose. As the build progresses, he will be able to assess the work and deal with your builders accordingly.

People who decide to get their house built in this way often do so because they want to deal with one firm rather than several sub-contractors. At least, that is the theory. In fact, as people often find out subsequently, their builder usually sub-contracts out the specialist tasks, and this can be when trouble strikes.

Clarify beforehand who the likely sub-contractors will be, and make sure that you and your professional adviser are happy with the quality of their work.

Two main advantages of using one builder for most or all of your build are: your house will get the NHBC Buildmark guarantee (assuming, of course, you use an NHBC builder); you will be charged no VAT.

The main disadvantage is that it will be more expensive than if you were to manage the build yourself, using sub-contractors.

Sub-contractors

For most self builders, ordering your own materials and dealing with sub-contractors is what self build is all about. This is where the savings are, because there is no overall profit element to go into a builder's pocket; it also gives you control of your own build.

Building this way may seem like the most enormous jump into the unknown. But take heart! Remember how you eat an elephant? A little at a time.

So, what exactly is involved with employing sub-contractors? Here are two basic ground rules to start you off:

- Always be careful about specifying the exact job; look for a specific quote. Get it in writing, accept it in writing and keep records.

- Get at least three quotes if you can. Of all the 'rules' associated with self build, this is the one that appears to be broken most frequently.

There are two reasons for this:

- The sub-contractor's local, I've used him before, I know I'm absolutely happy with him, and I wouldn't want to look elsewhere.

- He's got a nice face.

The first reason is fine, the second isn't. Where sub-contractors are concerned, you can be very vulnerable. Compare quotes; don't let yourself feel either pressurised or, worse, charmed into acceptance. Be as businesslike as possible. Remember, with sub-contractors, it is often a case of marriages being made in heaven and ending up in that place below.

Before hiring sub-contractors, find out a few things to your own satisfaction:

- **Are they NHBC registered? Or members of some other reputable body, such as a contractors' association?**

- **Do they guarantee their work?**

- **Can they take you to see work they have recently completed, and introduce you to previous satisfied customers?**

- **Do they have experience of timber frame construction?**

In drawing up your specification for the job, don't worry about using 'the right language'. There is a lot to be said for plain English. What matters is that your meaning is clear and unambiguous. Use words that everyone can understand, try to be as exact as you possibly can, cover all eventualities, and put everything in writing. This is to save misunderstandings later, and to stop your sub-contractor wailing: *"But you didn't ask for it!"*

Work through all the literature from the timber frame company, particularly the schedule of building and the working drawings, and keep referring to these. For instance, you could specify work for the roof along these lines:

"To fix all necessary felt, battens, Redland Rosemary clay tiles and sufficient ridge, valley and vent tiles to completely roof the whole house exactly as shown in Plan 10/93. Allow for all valley boards, and to fix all lead valleys and flashings, and coloured mortar beds for the verges and ridge tiles. All material to be supplied."

Make certain that the sub-contractor understands that he will not be charging you VAT, and that his invoices should be zero rated.

For large jobs – the bricklaying and roofing – the sub-contractor will want stage payments. The rule about stage payments is absolutely clear: they should be made for work that has been done, not for work that hasn't.

With sub-contractors, never pay in full up front. Either wait for the work to be finished, or agree beforehand what the stages for payment are: they should relate to the build (ie, the number of bricks laid), not the hours put in. Also make it clear beforehand that you will only make stage payments for satisfactory work, and that 'satisfactory' means that the work has been passed by the building inspector and/or your architect. Where sub-contractors both supply and fix, you will be asked to pay for materials on delivery. This is fair enough, but always insist on getting an invoice first.

Time is important so ask the sub-contractor to state in his quotation how long the work will take. Make it clear that if the contract over-runs, you will reduce your payment. Some sub-contractors may not accept this, but persevere. In a timber frame build, work proceeds at such a brisk pace that you simply cannot afford to allow the roofers to go off to another job for three weeks leaving yours unfinished (do I sound bitter? Well, it happened to us!).

If you are at all worried about drawing up your specifications, and sorting out the quotes, don't hesitate to get professional advice.

Each quote that you receive should be in writing, not on the back of a cigarette packet, and should be at least as detailed as your specification. It should also be a quote not an estimate. This is because an estimate is what it says it is, whereas a quote is fixed. It will usually be fixed for a specified period of time.

A time to hire . . .

Here are some of the most common pitfalls – and suggested ways out of them.

Extras

One continually sticky problem with sub-contractors is that even when you have agreed on the work to be done and on the payment for it, 'extras' arise. It can be very easy, during the course of a build, suddenly to see something that needs doing that you had not thought of before; it can be even easier to be talked into something that a keen sub-contractor (who wants to carry on working for you) thinks is a good idea, and somehow everyone's carried away on a wave of enthusiasm.

Unfortunately, enthusiasm can work out expensive.

Make it a rule that when 'extras' arise, the extra cost and time implications are put into writing by the sub-contractor, and agreed by you in writing. In fact, you can cover yourself against this possibility beforehand, by writing in your original letter of acceptance of his quote: *"If extra work crops up in the course of this contract, please do not go ahead without my specific agreement to it in writing."*

Under-estimates

Another common problem with sub-contractors is when they tell you that, unfortunately, they have under-estimated one bit of their work, and they are going to have to make adjustments, otherwise there will be nothing in it for them, their families will starve to death and it will all be your fault.

This can be a long and moving story, and it is terribly easy to give in. But don't be a sucker. Remind your sub-contractor that he gave you a firm quote, not an estimate. Harden your heart: it is, after all, his fault if he genuinely did under-estimate. Actually, he probably didn't: it is a sadly common ploy to give one price for a job in order to get it, and then try and get more when halfway through.

Some sub-contractors are more important than others, in that the quality of their work shows. In employing brickies and roofers, do not accept the cheapest quote, but the best prospect of top class work. Do ask to see samples of what they have done previously.

One more tip: never pay sub-contractors by the hour; that way, your money will run away with you. Pay them for specific work which has been done.

A lot of sub-contractors want to be paid in cash. Bricklayers, for instance, may quite unexpectedly demand their stage payments in cash on Fridays, which will involve you in irritating dashes to the bank in order to ensure that they are back on site on Monday.

Do clarify beforehand how your sub-contractors want to be paid, and make sure that the arrangement is both acceptable and convenient to you. Also make it clear that just because it's cash, there is no question of payments not being properly recorded by you.

With smaller sub-contractors – ie, the man who does your screeding – the situation is slightly different. He may be moonlighting, which is one thing; working in his own time at weekends, which is another; or simply reluctant to put earnings on a small one-off job through his books. In all such cases, there'll be nothing in writing, and of course payment will be in cash.

There is no doubt that if you pay cash, you can get work done both professionally and cheaply. But do weigh up the pros and cons of this kind of arrangement carefully. You need a high degree of trust for it to work.

Steer clear of the moonlighter – the man who is employed by someone else, but who has told his bosses he is 'off sick' whilst in reality he is working for you. If his bosses can't trust him, will you be able to? The chap who is self employed but doesn't want to declare his earnings is also a matter for your own conscience.

The real difficulty is, if you are paying cash, what is your comeback? Even with the smallest sub-contractors, it's best to choose carefully. Certainly, always withhold money until you are satisfied.

Finally, sub-contractors have been mentioned here on the assumption that you are employing them on a labour-only basis. It is always worth asking them for two quotes, for labour-only as well as for supply and fix.

Nine times out of ten, you will find you can buy materials cheaper than they can. There is, however, always that tenth time when a sub-contractor can negotiate a better deal than you can.

. . . and a time to fire

The real nightmare is when things go wrong. It is vitally important that mistakes and problems are picked up early and dealt with promptly. Obviously confrontation is never desirable, and while it should be avoided if possible, it may sometimes be inevitable. Remember, it is your money, your home being built, and at the end of the day, you are the boss. The best results are always achieved by being fair and pleasant; but never be afraid to assert yourself so that problems do not escalate.

There are five main problems:

1. Poor quality of work. If you are unhappy with the quality of work being done, say so. And, of course, don't pay. That really is your final weapon.

2. Case of the disappearing sub-contractor. The first tactic is to track him down and find out why. Be pleasant – sympathetic, even – but firm. If your sub-contractor has personal problems, be understanding. If he has grievances, you will need to sort them out. This is where having an architect or surveyor can be very helpful.

If your sub-contractor still fails to turn up to work, or you have not managed to speak to him, you will have to consider what to do next. Some sub-contractors are much more dispensable than others. You may even be glad to see the back of them.

Others are vital – roofers, for instance, who are halfway through the job. If all else fails, write by recorded letter, and give a deadline by which he is to turn up on site and finish the job. Explain in this letter that it will probably cost more to get this job finished by having to call in a second sub-contractor, and that you will be charging the difference between the eventual cost and the original quote. This may have the desired effect.

If not, and if a considerable sum of money is involved in the work, check the position with your solicitor to ensure that the sub-contractor won't be alleging that it's you who have broken the contract.

3. He prevaricates. This is considered the worst problem of all, because it is so hard to deal with. A sub-contractor who slopes off early, or is trying to keep several jobs on the go, all the time promising that he will be back on your site to finish off 'tomorrow', is someone who knows how to raise other people's blood pressure.

As we all know, procrastination is the thief of time; it is also the thief of money, and one sub-contractor's prevarication can wreck a carefully planned building programme.

What do you do? Be firm and insistent. Withhold money, issue an ultimatum in writing and let him

know that if there are financial consequences because of any further delay, he will be held responsible.

4. Getting a new sub-contractor. Getting a second sub-contractor to finish off work done by the first is often difficult although it can be done. Basically, it's best to avoid the necessity by choosing correctly in the first place, putting everything in writing and making time of the essence.

5. Be a good boss. The above paints the worst scenario. But there is absolutely no reason why you and your sub-contractors should not all get along perfectly well.

That means operating in a fair and reasonable manner, not withholding money unreasonably, and paying what is due promptly. Good relationships with good sub-contractors are both possible and desirable, and most self builders end up with a team of people they can call friends. Sub-contractors, like anybody else, like being praised and thanked for good work.

Like anyone else, they'll respond to smiles, friendly conversation, and plenty of cups of tea.

Oh, and most important of all, they ALL take two sugars!

Checklist when employing sub-contractors

- **Specify the job you want done in writing**
- **Get them to quote, not estimate, and make sure they give firm quotes**
- **Make sure they state a time schedule and realise the importance of sticking to it**
- **Never pay in full up front**
- **Agree any stage payments before you start**
- **Stage payments should be for work completed, not for work that hasn't been done**
- **Make final payment conditional on approval by the building inspector, or the architect or surveyor**
- **Ensure pleasant working conditions on site**

Site management

An important part of managing your own build is looking after the site and ensuring that everythinmg runs smoothly.

There are four main factors which you should consider at the start of the project.

- **Access**

- **Services**

- **Handling and storage of materials**

- **Safety and security**

It is vital that you have a good, solid surface access right up to your building plot. In the early days of your build, you can expect some very large lorries – delivering cement, bricks, tiles, and your timber frame.

Your house will probably arrive on the back of the largest lorry (or even two lorries) your road has ever seen. Do make sure that your new home can be delivered. Check the width of your access, potentially difficult bends, and heights of any low bridges in the immediate vicinity.

It is often not worth laying a final surface on your driveway, but it is worth making sure that, no matter what the weather does, lorries and diggers will be able to get up and down it without getting stuck.

Services – water, electricity, phone, gas, Liquefied Petroleum Gas, oil – will be needed on site. Not all of them, of course, but you will not be able to start your build without the first two, so you must arrange for these to be laid on.

Work out where materials are going to be delivered and stored. You will need to keep a good clear space at the front of the actual building site, so that Readymix lorries can back straight up, and when your timber frame arrives, it can be offloaded straight on to the slab.

Allocate areas which are convenient but not in anyone's way for materials to be delivered and stored.

If your site is narrow, with no room at the sides or in front to store materials, then large consignments (bricks and tiles) should be delivered before the foundations are dug, and stored in the back garden.

With a timber frame, storing materials is thankfully not the headache it is with a brick and block house. After all, your house will be weathertight in a fraction of the time, and can store its own materials – paints, plasterboards, tools, and so on.

Even so, storage of materials requires thought. In particular, plasterboard should not be allowed to stand unprotected outside. If it is delivered before you are ready for it, cover it with tarpaulin. It should not be allowed to get damp.

If site security is likely to be a problem, a lockable shed, caravan, or container of some sort is a must; if it can do double duty as a workman's caff, so much the better.

If site security is a real worry, there is really no way round it other than arranging to be on site as much as possible – preferably with a large dog! Living on site for the duration of the build may be uncomfortable in a caravan, but it definitely has its benefits.

Keeping your site as clean and tidy as possible is a must. You may regard yourself as the boss of your self build, but in terms of chores, your tasks are the most menial of all.

Sweeping up, clearing away unwashed mugs, ensuring that all rubbish is promptly removed, and having clearly defined areas for mixing concrete, makes for a site which is quite simply easier and more efficient to work.

Site insurance is important, and before work starts, you should arrange cover for public liability and employer's liability. This should relate to:-

- **Accidents** on site.

- **Third party cover.** If a piece of scaffolding falls on top of your neighbour's car, it could be expensive. If it also causes an accident, the results don't bear thinking about.

- **Theft.** Insure your tools and building materials.

There are one or two package insurances for self builders; or you could arrange your own cover. The crucial thing is to arrange it before work starts. But the whole question of site accidents is not merely a matter of taking out insurance: safety procedures are absolutely essential. Remember, everyone on site MUST wear a hard hat at all times (that includes you); and never let children think of the site as a playground. Safety on a self build site is largely a matter of good practice and common sense, but if you want advice on the legalities, contact your local Health and Safety Executive (number in the local phone book).

Buying materials

As said before, a quantity surveyor's report can be worth its weight in gold. Okay, not gold. It will probably cost you about £500. One or two specialist services operate (advertised in *Build It*). It is well worth your while to get a list of every material you will need for the complete build of your house.

Without this, your options are to enlist the help of your timber frame supplier, or to go to a friendly builder's merchant. All are indeed helpful, but in varying degrees, and at the end of the day, they are not quantity surveyors who can specify exactly what you need in order to build the design of your choice in the materials of your choice, right down to the last nail and bag of cement.

Run the risk of over or under ordering, and you will be hard put to know which is worse. Under ordering can be just as wasteful as over ordering. A shortfall of tiles here, and not enough bricks there, means a delay in sub-contractors being able to finish off, and having to pay extra for small deliveries. Over-order, and you may have to pay for materials to be collected and returned; or you will have to waste time in returning them yourself.

Builder's merchants seem extraordinarily daunting places when you first start going to them, but familiarity breeds affection (well, almost). It is worth your while going to two or three to look at their prices and services, and to explain that you are building a house which will require £40,000 worth of building materials. You should then have the satisfaction of watching their eyes brighten.

The days of 'trade only' or even of 'trade discounts' are over. Any smart builder's merchant will not want you shopping round for bargains, and will want to offer you a good deal.

You should be able to set up an account which, if you settle monthly, should give you 30 days grace on payment (something that could come in very useful if you yourself are having to wait for stage payments from the building society). Builder's merchants will usually offer a same-day delivery service; and if you give them a copy of your plans, can be a mine of information about building materials and prices.

Prices of building materials can be a mystery. Some building materials, notably bricks, actually have no recommended retail price. If you are really keen, you could get hold of Hutchins' Price Schedules (£45 for a set of 12, or £12 per schedule) which estimate current prices of over 6,000 items. The address is in the listings section of this book which appears at the end.

Hiring equipment

Hire specialists make life easy for the self builder, and it is worth getting their catalogues before starting a self build. The items you may need include: pumps, concrete mixers, generators, surveying equipment, and all sorts of machinery with names which sound very strange to the novice builder.

Generally speaking, your sub-contractors will probably know better than you, what needs hiring. Your main job as site manager will be to ensure that the hired equipment is returned promptly and used safely. If goggles, helmets, ear defenders, dust masks, gloves and steel reinforced footwear should be worn, make sure that they are.

The most important item of hire to any self builder is undoubtedly the scaffolding which you will need to get from a specialist scaffolding firm. Check with your timber frame supplier what their scaffolding requirements are. They may make their own arrangements; they may not. If your erectors do need you to arrange scaffolding, it will need to be on site very early on – probably on the second day of the frame erection.

Scaffolding is not a DIY job. It needs to be supplied, safely erected, and then adjusted in what are called 'lifts' as the build proceeds.

Scaffolding always seems to be on site longer and cost more than anyone ever tells you, so be warned! It can also cause a phenomenal amount of irritation when the bricklayers demand it is taken up a lift right now this minute, and the scaffolding company say they can't come until tomorrow afternoon.

There ought to be a way of pre-planning all this, but sometimes with scaffolding, all you can do is be pragmatic!

Time schedule

It's important to take advantage of the speed offered by timber frame. But contingent on this is the ability to ensure that your sub-contractors are ready to start, and your materials ready in time.

The following time schedule will help. Put in your own dates, and count back six week for the purposes of ordering materials. Ask for them to be delivered a week before you need them, and keep checking on delivery. Allow the same, or longer, to arrange your sub-contractors; maintain telephone contact with them to ensure that they too will be on site on the agreed date.

This form shows you how to draw up a timetable for your build. As the manager, it is important to ensure that everything occurs within the period specified.

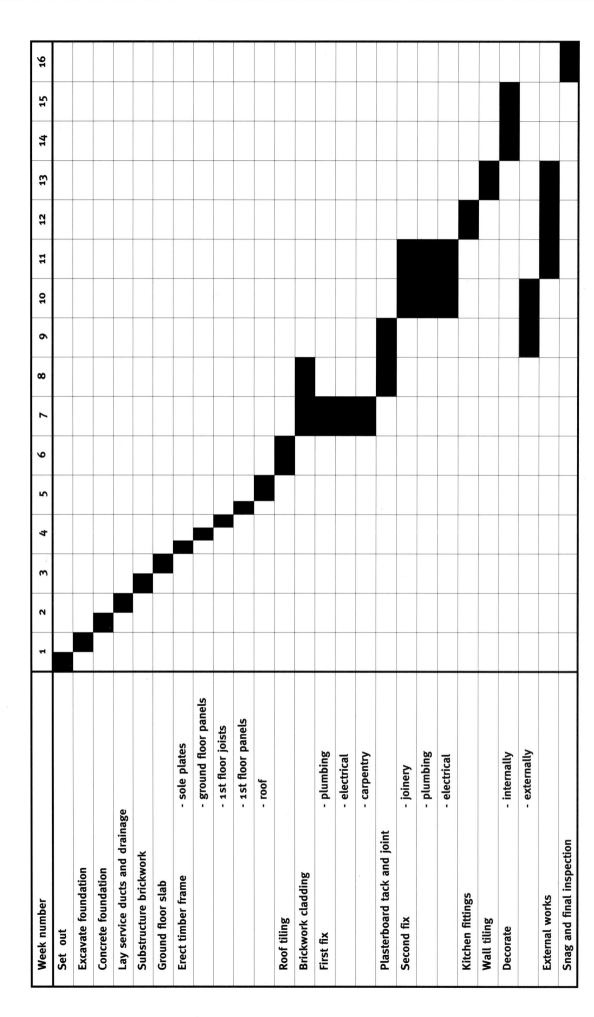

Week number	1	2	3	4	5	6	7	8	9	10	11	12	13	14	15	16
Set out	■															
Excavate foundation		■														
Concrete foundation			■													
Lay service ducts and drainage				■												
Substructure brickwork				■												
Ground floor slab					■											
Erect timber frame - sole plates					■											
- ground floor panels						■										
- 1st floor joists						■										
- 1st floor panels							■									
- roof							■									
Roof tiling								■								
Brickwork cladding								■								
First fix - plumbing								■								
- electrical								■								
- carpentry								■								
Plasterboard tack and joint									■							
Second fix - joinery										■	■					
- plumbing										■	■					
- electrical										■	■					
Kitchen fittings												■				
Wall tiling												■				
Decorate - internally													■			
- externally															■	
External works										■	■		■			
Snag and final inspection																■

Part 3
How to...

The pre-planning stage is over, and the build itself is ready to start. This section examines the actual stages of construction, starting with preparation of the plot, and finishing at the point where you are ready to move in.

Chapter 11: Preparing the plot

Many plots need to be cleared of wilderness, trees and rubbish before you can start building. You will want to preserve as many trees and shrubs as possible, taking out only those which are actually in the way, or too close to where the foundations will go. As a general rule, anyone can cut down trees on their own land, provided there is no preservation order in force. Trees near boundaries sometimes present ownership problems. A tree is normally owned by the person on whose land it grows, regardless of how many roots or branches protrude above or below the neighbouring land. You are entitled by law to lop overhanging branches provided you return the cuttings to the owner on the other side of the fence.

Some trees are more of a threat than others on a building plot, especially on clay-based soils. A good rule of thumb is that the safe distance from buildings is at least the height of the mature tree. Trees which need large amounts of water pose the greatest threat. Poplar, willow, horse chestnut and sycamore are very invasive water-seekers, and obviously you don't want them invading your drainage system.

As a tree grows, its roots and base expand. This can be enough to lift light structures (paving, kerbing, and even single storey buildings such as garages and porches) but not usually house foundations, because the tree roots will distort round rigid objects. Paths and drives can be damaged by trees with a lot of surface roots such as ash, cherry, pine and birch.

The real threat to foundations is the movement of soil, particularly clay, around nearby trees. In the summer, the soil shrinks as the trees draw up moisture; in winter or when it rains, the ground swells. This continual movement is what caused so much subsidence and structural damage in the great drought of the mid-seventies. It proved very expensive for the insurance companies, caused premiums to rise, and has resulted in much greater attention to foundation design.

Unfortunately, the threat of subsidence cannot be solved simply by felling. This itself can cause 'heave', which can crack walls and foundations. Heaving occurs when a tree is removed; because it is no longer absorbing water, the ground slowly swells with water. If you are in any doubt as to whether trees are better left or felled, ask your building inspector or your surveyor for advice.

Stumps left after felling can leave huge craters. Burn, dig or pull them out with a winch, tractor, or the local tug of war team. But be thorough. The complete removal of a stump involves digging up a large area to get rid of the roots, and even then roots may be exposed when the foundations are dug. If these are spotted by the building inspector, he may want the foundations to go down deeper.

> **Checklist:**
>
> - **Trees with high water demand are oak, willow, elm and poplars. Least problematic trees are magnolia, birch and beech.**
> - **Oak and elm grow up to 24 metres in height, willow to 22 metres, and poplar to 30 metres.**
> - **If your plot has large trees which are closer to the house than their height, it is a good idea to get professional advice or talk to Building Central.**
> - **Trees with moderate water demand are: ash, cherry, hawthorn, horse chestnut, laburnum, lime, maple, sycamore, apple, pear, plum and yew. The tallest of these are ash, cherry, horse chestnut, lime, sycamore and maple, all growing to around 20 metres.**

Access and services

Access to your building site needs to be wide enough for deliveries, and dry at all times. You should also consider the availability of your other services at the same time. These are:

- **water**
- **mains gas**
- **electricity**
- **sewerage – either a link to the main drainage system, a septic tank or cesspool**
- **surface water drainage - to mains or soakaways**
- **telephone**
- **cable TV**
- **oil**
- **LPG**

Make early contact with the various utilities to arrange for services to be laid on, and decide where

A Border Oak cottage built on a challenging site - note the sloping land and wooded surroundings.

each will enter the site and, eventually, your house. As manager of your self build, your object is to co-ordinate the services as much as possible, so that trench digging can be carried out at the same time and kept to a minimum.

Water

You may need a temporary standpipe for 'building water' as it is called, and even though you will fix it up yourself, there will be a charge for connection, probably around £40. You are also responsible for laying the water pipe yourself, from the edge of the highway, at the prescribed depth. If there is already a water supply on site, be thankful – a hosepipe will do very nicely.

When your house is ready to be connected to the water supply, you will have to pay for the privilege – around £500 is the current connection charge; you will also have to pay around £400 to be connected up for sewerage. Charges vary considerably across the country, and from one situation to another. Quotes of £3,000 are not unknown, and not suprisingly, some self builders prefer to lay on their own supplies from bore holes. However, if you do this, you will not escape bureaucracy. Indeed, you will have a whole battery of around sixty different tests to pay for (around £400), to prove to the local environmental health department that your drinking supply is wholesome, and you will have to pay an annual monitoring fee (currently about £65).

Another problem with water authorities that is worth mentioning is that they can be very slow; it doesn't do any good to complain because they are, of course, a monopoly, and there have been cases of people completing their builds and moving in several weeks before they are connected to a water supply.

Power

The gas and electricity companies will lay their own supplies, in trenches roughly one third of a metre deep from the highway to the boxes which will go on the outside of your house, and where your supplies enter your house. A temporary supply of electricity is extremely useful during the build, and probably essential if you are living on site in a caravan. Tell the electricity board what you want, so that you can comply with their requirements. To establish a safe supply of electricity, even a temporary one, is a job for a professional electrician.

Telephone

British Telecom will simply give you a cable in a conduit, and let you get on with it. You should lay it in a trench which, again, should be one third of a metre deep.

Engineer's report

Plots vary tremendously in their buildability, and some have been something else in a previous existence – woodland, rubbish dumps, or made up with fill or hardcore. Believe it or not, I have come across two sites in different parts of the country which were once bomb craters, something which was only discovered when they started to dig the foundations, and found that they had to go down three to four metres. They would have known if they had had an engineer's report first.

If you know of, or suspect that there might be, any problems, get an engineer's report, so that you can establish how stable the ground is going to be underneath your foundations.

Your architect or surveyor will advise you on whether to call in an engineer or not, or you could ask the building inspector. Many self builders, rightly, believe that getting the foundations right is so important that they would want an engineer's report anyway.

The engineer will get sample holes dug which are at least one metre deep. If the soil at the very bottom of these sample holes is loose, soft or silty, special foundations will be indicated. The engineer will also advise on the implications of trees on or surrounding the site. He will also test the soil for the presence of sulphates. Sulphates can eat into ordinary concrete, so if their presence is established, the engineer will advise you to use sulphate resisting cement.

An engineer's report won't be cheap but it can save you money. While it will often show the need for extra precautions with your foundations, it may equally show that your foundations don't need to be as deep or as complicated as the building inspector believes.

Groundwork and foul drainage

The day that the groundworker in his JCB rumbles on to your site is a great one, because it is the day when you feel you are finally starting. This is your first sub-contractor, and the very first person to take two sugars in his tea!

The term groundwork covers a lot of activity from creating an access, to taking the topsoil off the site where you will build your house, to digging your foul drainage system and excavating your foundations.

Removing the topsoil is a major event. It does not have to be removed with pinpoint accuracy. Some people mark out the area with pegs, others simply agree beforehand the area to be excavated. It is important to have a wide enough area excavated – all round the perimeter of your foundations will become very messy, and at the end of the build, it is easier to clear it up and then replace the topsoil.

What are you going to do with the excavated topsoil? With any luck, your garden will be large enough for it to be dumped and indeed, you may have already planned a rockery or some grand landscaping feature to be constructed out of all the excacated subsoil you are also going to have to deal with, as well as the topsoil. If not, hopefully you will find someone crying out for it. It is, however, an infallible law that when you have topsoil to give away, no one wants it. When, however, you want it, you can't get it for love or money!

Drainage is not always as foul as you might think. In other words, don't confuse surface water drainage system with your sewerage system. The two used to be one and the same: all waste water, whether from your loos or your gutters, went into the same system. Now they are separated and must be kept separated. Possibly, your surface water will go into a main drain. If not, all the rainwater that lands on and immediately around your house is drained away into soakaways – large, deep holes filled with gravel and/or rubble, and big enough to cope with the heaviest rainfall, which will then seep away. You will probably need at least two soakaways, either at the front and back of your house, or at either side, and at least five metres away.

The foul waste will go into the main drainage system, or into a septic tank or, just possibly, a cesspool (your building inspector will advise you here). A septic tank treats and reduces down the foul waste, using biological processes; a cesspool merely holds the waste and whilst a septic tank will need emptying only rarely (perhaps just once a year), a cesspool will need emptying perhaps as often as once or twice a week. Modern septic tanks

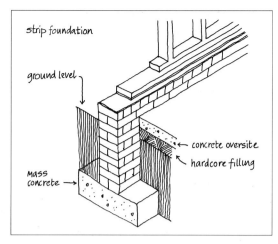

Standard strip foundation.

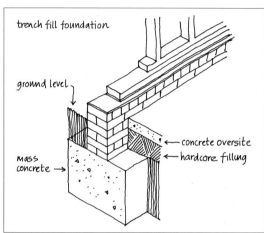

Trench fill foundation.

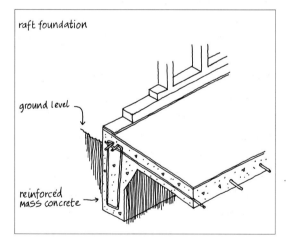

Raft foundation.

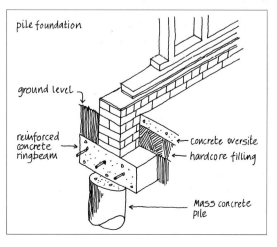

Pile foundation.

are clean, unobtrusive and so efficient that their manufacturers are fond of boasting that water that has been processed is fit to drink. Most of us would prefer to take their word for it! At any rate, this is a competitive market where manufacturers seem only too pleased to help you design a drainage system which will get the blessing of the Building Regulations people, and of the water authority.

All drains should obey two rules: they should drain away downhill, not uphill; and they should be roddable along their entire length which means that you should be able to get at them; hence the need for inspection chambers (manholes).

When paying your groundwork sub-contractor, it is usual to withhold a small percentage from the final payment until the whole drainage system has been tested and passed by the building inspector.

Foundations

Once the approximate area of your foundations has had the topsoil skimmed, it will be time for setting out. This is the exact marking out, on the ground, using pegs and string, of the precise floor area of the house you will be building.

This is a job you may like to undertake yourself, or you can get a surveyor to do it. It is probably a good idea to choose the latter course every time. This a critically important part of your project, and one that just has to be right. Timber frame is such a highly engineered product that there is simply no room for error. Bear this in mind before deciding whether you really want this responsibility.

When the setting out is done, you will be able to see the exact ground area of your house, with the corners marked by lengths of timber known as profile boards. These are used as an aid to the digger driver who will now excavate the trenches for your foundations. You will have the same problem with the excavated subsoil as you had with the topsoil, but more so. The cheapest option is to keep this 'spoil' on your own site and use it for backfilling. Otherwise, you will end up paying for it to be taken away.

There are several different kinds of foundations. A timber frame house is a lightweight structure compared with one of masonry construction, and this should be an advantage as far as foundations are concerned. In practice, building inspectors are a cautious lot and operate on the principle of better safe than sorry.

The main types of foundations are:

- **Strip footings**
- **Trench fill** (or deep strip)
- **Reinforced concrete raft**
- **Piles, with reinforced concrete ground beams**

Generally speaking, the self builder will be concerned with the first two types. The second two types are for more difficult sites; they are both reinforced foundations, and would have to be specifically designed by a structural engineer.

- **Strip footings** are traditional foundations. Trenches one metre deep are dug and filled with nine inches – or strips – of concrete to take the weight of the house. The one-metre depth is the standard for foundations, but the building inspector may ask for them to go deeper.

On top of the concrete, walls are built up with bricks or blocks, until they are brought to a level out of the ground. The effect at this stage is of a raised rectangular box. The position of these underground trenches and walls corresponds with all the load bearing walls which will be built above. If you are having an Aga, or similar cooker, this too will have its own concrete filled support in the foundations; fireplaces will also need their own foundations.

Hardcore is then used to fill in the foundations. This needs to be compacted in, and drains and pipework also need to be laid in now. The compacted hardcore surface is then covered with a damp proof membrane (dpm) – a thick polythene sheet, which in turn is linked to the damp proof course (dpc) in the walls. This is to stop damp rising out of the ground.

The next step is to make a solid floor – see below.

- **Trench fill,** sometimes called deep strip. These are similar to standard strip foundations, but the trenches are filled almost to the top with concrete. Trench fill foundations save time, because there is less brick and blockwork to be built up. The trenches themselves are narrower but deeper. Deep trench fill foundations are indicated where the house is built next to trees whose roots may be invasive.

- **Raft foundations** consist of a reinforced slab sitting under the surface, taking the weight of the building. Raft foundations are used on really difficult, often variable ground – for instance, on a site right by a river, which was prone to flooding, a raft foundation was used; the object of a raft foundation is to spread the load of the structure above on to a wide area of ground.

- **Pile foundations** are needed where you have to go some way down to find good, load-bearing ground. Pile foundations are holes that go through the bad ground and into the solid, and which are then filled with concrete. These piles are usually needed at each corner and at about twelve foot intervals around the perimeter. Reinforced ground beams then go on top.

Floors

The foundations are very often finished off with a solid concrete floor.

- **Ground bearing slab:** The traditional method is to pour a six inch concrete slab over all the hardcore between the foundation walls. This slab will later be finished off by a thin, smooth floor surface known as the screed which is usually about two inches thick. If you are insulating, this will take the form of solid slabs of insulating material laid under the screed, in which case the screed must either be thicker or include a weldmesh reinforcement.

- **Block and beam floor.** This is when beams of concrete are laid across the floor like railway sleepers and filled in with blocks. The gaps between are then grouted. Insulation goes on top of this surface (if you want it) and then the flooring of your choice – chipboard nailed on to battens is usual, or you may use screed as described above.

Building inspectors and warrantors prefer block and beam floors to slab because, before they became prevalent, 85 per cent of all claims to the NHBC were to do with failure of the actual floor slab which was prone to heaving and cracking as the hardcore beneath moved. Because a block and beam floor is essentially a suspended floor, this does not happen. For self builders the big advantage of a block and beam floor is that there is no lengthy wait for huge quantities of concrete to dry; nor is a wet screed essential. Thus the floor surface is always dry and there is no hold up in the building schedule.

- **A timber joist floor** is similar to the upper floors with a chipboard, or similar, deck nailed, to give a suspended floor. Insulation is mineral wool put between the joists.

To conclude this section, foundations are unpredictable and famously difficult to cost out in advance. Even professionals building for themselves have found their foundations going way, way over budget. This is where you need a very healthy contingency in your budget. If you are lucky and you haven't needed it, offer up a silent prayer – you may be able to afford gold plated bath taps after all!

Chapter 12: Out of the ground!

Your groundworkers have now finished and you have what is called an oversite (no, not an oversight, and let's hope there haven't been any).

Before going any further, a word about damp proofing. Both damp proof membranes and damp proof courses must be carefully laid, and must lap to produce an uninterrupted barrier. As we have just seen, the groundworkers will have laid down the dpm. Depending on your foundations, either they or your bricklayers will also be responsible for the external wall dpc. More probably, the dpc will be put in by your bricklayers as they start taking the bricks up to window level.

- As manager of your site you should ensure that both the dpc and the dpm are laid properly, and that the material is not punctured or damaged during construction. In many cases where rising dampness has been identified, it has been because the dpc in the wall did not cover the full width of the brickwork.

- Ensure that your dpm laps at the joists under your slab sufficiently (by at least 150mm) and that any

punctures are sealed. Dpcs in walls should lap by at least 100mm, should be wide enough to project very slightly on the external face of the brickwork, and must never be pointed over. It's also vital that the dpc is at the correct level, which is at least 150mm above soil level.

With your foundations complete, you now have a smooth, solid base on which your timber frame can be erected.

This should have been ordered in good time, to arrive as soon as the foundations are ready. Your supplier will probably have telephoned a week or so beforehand to check that everything is in place. The supplier will not wish to load your frame up if you are not ready to receive it. If you put off the delivery at the last moment, you might have to pay a financial penalty.

You should also ensure that scaffolding or any lifting machinery that the erection team needs, has been arranged.

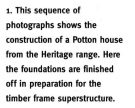

1. This sequence of photographs shows the construction of a Potton house from the Heritage range. Here the foundations are finished off in preparation for the timber frame superstructure.

1.

If scaffolding is needed, it will almost certainly be wanted on the second day of erection. You will need to organise the scaffolding to be delivered and (probably) erected early that morning in order to avoid delay with the frame.

It's advisable to book the scaffolding at least a month beforehand, and confirm the time, date and place the week before and then the day before.

Check, check and check again!

It is worth having your foundations checked out before you finally agree to your frame being loaded ready for delivery. There is nothing worse than having the frame delivered, the erection team on site, and then realising that the dimensions of your foundations are slightly askew and the levels are wrong. Yes, it happens! And if it does, it causes delay.

The contracts manager from your timber frame supplier might well be happy to check your slab. You could even make it a condition of your becoming a customer that he does so. This is a very good idea. Otherwise, get your foundations checked out by a surveyor.

Arrival of the frame

Your frame will come on a huge lorry, and will be unloaded with a great deal of logic, so that everything is where it needs to be for erection. At this stage, it will look exactly like a giant jigsaw puzzle and you will wonder how it can ever be put together.

The first thing the erection team will do is to check the dimensions and levels of the slab or floor. Then they will start work. Their first task will be installing the sole plate.

This is a framework of special preservative treated timber, fixed around the perimeter. The erectors will pay a lot of attention to making sure that the sole plate is exactly right: if there are even tiny variations in levels, they will use material, such as small pieces of slate, to pack beneath it.

Once the sole plate is in place, your house will start to go up. First, the ground floor loadbearing panels and joists are put up; the first floor deck is then fixed to these joists. The first floor wall panels are next. Then the roof trusses are fixed. And there is your frame! Assuming that the panels have all arrived complete with breather membrane, it now

2. As a result of the high water table, raised foundations had to be used.

3. The timber sole plate is now in place and ready to take the timber frame superstructure.

4. Normally no more than three people are needed to lift the post and beam superstructure into place - here someone else has been roped in to help.

5. The ground floor panel, complete with ready-glazed windows, being fitted by the erection team.

only needs the roof trusses to be felted and battened, and your house is weathertight, allowing trades to work in dry conditions inside.

Frames, sizes of wall panels, and work methods differ. Some wall panels will arrive complete with windows fully double or triple glazed. Some erection teams will want cranes to lift the panels or certain beams into place; check beforehand.

The photographic sequence on pages 104-113 shows the building of a Potton Heritage house. The construction includes load bearing posts and beams, but the external walls and the rest of the build are exactly the same as for a wall panel timber frame.

Post and truss

If you are having a Border Oak (or similar) post and truss timber frame, the method of erection will be different from platform frame, since this is a matter of raising a skeletal frame as opposed to wall panels.

With this type of frame, work starts in just the same way, with the soleplate being bedded on to the perimeter of the base and across the slab. Full height corner posts and shorter ground floor studs

are placed in the soleplate. These are propped in position, and receive the girding rail (which 'girds' together the entire perimeter of the building at first floor level). The rest of the frame is put together in a series of massive trusses, joists and beams.

This will in fact be the second time that the Border Oak frame has been assembled. It has already had a complete test assembly on the 'framing ground' at plant; once assembled, each part is incised with Roman numerals, disassembled and then delivered.

The erectors then raise the frame again, following the Roman numerals – literally, in other words, by numbers.

It will fit!

Whatever type of timber frame method you use, there will be no question of it not fitting together, because it has of course been engineered to do just that, and the erectors will be using a nailing schedule so that everything goes up in exactly the right order.

When the erection team have nailed the last nail and departed, the silence will seem almost unnatural. Your house is now ready for its next stages – its hat

6. Once the first floor panels have been set in place, the frame for the second floor can begin to take shape.

7. And after the second floor panels come the roof trusses and a recognisable house begins to emerge!

8. After the internal studs have been set in place, the next stage is the first fix plumbing and electrics.

6.

7.

8.

and overcoat. The hat, or roof, comes first. One reason is to make the structure waterproof, the other is to ensure that the structure is properly loaded, or weighted down.

Roof

Unless you are having your house thatched – and there is no reason why you shouldn't – the next stage is felting and battening, by your roofing sub-contractor.

This can and should be done just as soon as your shell is up, to form the first line of defence against the weather. Felting and battening usually takes only a day or two.

The next step is for the roof to be loaded with tiles – when all the tiles are carried up and stacked in regular piles all over the slopes of the roof ready for use – and then for the tiling itself. Depending on the size and complexity of your roof – and the weather – tiling should not take long: a week perhaps. Choosing the tiles will, without a doubt, have taken you a lot longer. There are hundreds of different tiles and slates on the market today and it is very hard deciding what will please your own aesthetic tastes, the planners, and your budget.

In conservation areas, tiles are a remarkably sensitive subject. You will almost certainly be expected to use whichever material – slate, stone or clay – predominates. But in any case, the planners can insist on you using a particular material. The roof's design will also be a factor in deciding on which tiles you use. Slates and larger tiles – such as clay pantiles, concrete profiled tiles and slates – tend to suit simple roof shapes; hips, valleys and small roof sections are difficult to form without complicated cutting. The minimum pitch (angle of slope) of your roof may also preclude certain types of tile. For example, clay plain tiles should not be used below 40°, nor concrete plain tiles below 30°, except in very special circumstances – always make sure you understand the technical specification of tiles (and for that matter, all your other building materials).

Don't be afraid to get advice, whether from your architect, the timber frame supplier, builder's merchant, or from the tile manufacturers.

For your roof, you will also need to buy fittings (the perimeter tiles for the ridge, hips, valleys and eaves) and accessories such as ventilation products to comply with Building Regulations.

9.

10.

9. Dormer windows are an important feature of this house. Here the roof trusses are being fitted, ready to take them.

10. A close-up of the roof shows how the dormer windows extend from the roof trusses.

11.

12.

11. A section of the roof showing the sprocket in place and the fly mesh fitted.

12. The first floor joists in place ready to take the decking.

Ridge and hip tiles have either a rounded or an angular profile, or you can choose decorative ridge tiles such as Fleur-de-Lys. Some manufacturers will make any shape you want, so long they can produce it, and you are prepared to pay for it!

Traditional ridge and hip tiles have to be bedded in mortar, but there are now 'dry' versions fixed mechanically using clips and screws and which offer better wind resistance.

All domestic roofs must, by law, be adequately ventilated, so to do the job properly, make sure you (or your roofing contractor) order sufficient eaves and high level ventilation products from your merchant.

You can ventilate the roof at the ridge or at high level with minimal visual disruption to the roofline. Several manufacturers offer ventilating ridge units and low profile ventilation tiles or slates in colours which match the main tiles.

Bricks

Until you became a self builder, it's likely that bricks will have counted amongst the world's most boring subjects. Suddenly, all that changes; not only are you about to discover the untold attractions of bricks, but a whole new vocabulary too.

You can of course clad your timber frame in a variety of ways. But brick – and with at least 1,200 different varieties, Britain has more bricks than anywhere else in the world – is most people's choice. However, timber frames can equally be clad in stone, weatherboarding, tilehanging or have a rendered finish; the outer cladding can also combine brick with tile hanging, or with stone or other features.

This is the stage at which you become completely obsessed, because whatever you choose, you must choose well. The external cladding of your house is the face it will show to the outside world.

Bricks will probably account for only six per cent of the total cost of your self build, but will contribute about 75 per cent of the overall look and feel of your house. So it is vital that your bricks are not just attractive but are also expertly laid. This means you should take as much care choosing your bricklayers as the bricks. First, the bricks. Although as a builder of a timber frame home, you will be choosing your bricks largely for their aesthetic

13. Metal back boxes fitted during the first fix electrics are now waiting for the second fix sockets.

13.

14.

14. Once the first fix plumbing and electrics are in place, the noggings must be fitted before the plasterboard is set up.

15. The inglenook fireplace, with its intricate brickwork, starts to take shape.

15.

16.

16. A bricklayer lays the plinth brick wall surrounding the panels.

qualities, they will have to be approved not just by you but also by the planners, and they must conform to Building Regulations. You may have to think twice if you want to use old bricks: a number of local authorities have refused permission because the strength, durability, water absorption and frost resistance of these bricks are all unknown.

In recent years, manufacturers have invested huge sums in developing attractive facing bricks, which can be used creatively to express individuality and style.

Bricks come in an enormous range of colours, from browns and reds through to buffs and yellows; there are plain colours, multis and blends; there are also bricks with a variety of flecks and colours within each individual brick. There are also smooth faced, sand-faced and heavily textured bricks.

You can achieve further creativity by your choice of mortar. Mortar has a decorative as well as a structural function, and if you choose a mortar with a pigmented sand added to it, you can use coloured mortar. If you want to use a coloured mortar, test it against your choice of brick. Most, but not all,

bricks are clay. Because of differences in mineral content and manufacturing processes, clay bricks vary markedly, not just in colour and texture, but in strength, density and durability. There are also bricks made from concrete, and calcium silicate, and they have a uniform appearance. If you don't like uniformity, you won't like these!

Assuming that you will want clay, you could go for one of the replica bricks which are now made – they look similar to the old bricks, but have been manufactured to modern standards.

Hand made bricks, as distinct from simulated machine made bricks, are probably what most self builders would really like, given the cash. These have a completely individual look, with a natural variation in colour and texture, so that your new house will immediately look appealingly mature.

You could also find out what bricks are made locally, since there are still (thankfully) some small, privately owned brickworks using their own clays and firing methods. Your local builder's merchant may have some helpful suggestions, and it's a good idea to feast on as much manufacturers' literature as possible. Gather together as many brick samples

17.

17. The house is now on the verge of completion. The roof has been felted and battened, the chimney and the feature timbers are in place and the render has been fitted.

as you can, and see what each looks like in different lights. When you have finally chosen, or at least narrowed your choice, take your sample bricks in to the local planning office for approval.

How many bricks will you need? As a rough guide, a 2,000 square foot house will need 15,000 bricks, which could cost you anything from £135 per thousand to £400 per thousand.

In your quest for the perfect brick, you will come across some mystifying expressions. If you want to nod your head knowledgeably, these are the most common of the facing bricks (which are the ones you want on the exterior of your home).

- **Wirecut bricks:** Made by a continuous column of clay being cut by wire, after which texture is added. Highly automated production makes these the cheapest of facing bricks. Cheap – emphatically – does not mean nasty. There are some excellent ranges of wirecut bricks, offering a high degree of consistent quality and durability in attractive colours and textures.

- **Stock bricks:** Traditional type, slightly irregular shape, made with a mechanised moulding process known as soft mud moulding.

- **Handmade bricks:** Literally made by hand. They have a distinctive creased face known as a 'smile' which gives a house a happy expression (yes, honestly!). Of course, if the bricks are laid the wrong way up, your house will look as if it is in a permanent sulk.

- **Specials:** Made for a particular purpose and used to create interesting features, for instance for window surrounds. One 'special' it's always nice for self builders to get is the date brick, produced by some brick companies. Give it pride of place, so that future historians will know at a glance that your house was built in 1993 or whenever! Many manufacturers have comprehensive collections of specials.

- **Fletton bricks:** Made from Oxford clay, require little firing, and are one of the cheapest of the clay bricks.

As well as facing bricks, there are also common bricks, used for general construction work but which are not intended to offer an attractive appearance, while engineering bricks are strong, rather than pretty and can be used for foundations, manholes and sewers.

18. Tiling proceeds apace and the roof is swiftly completed.

18.

19. The Eswa underfloor heating blanket is now in place.

19.

20. The vapour barrier is now installed and the walls insulated before the plasterboard is fitted.

20.

When choosing facing clay bricks, make sure they conform to current UK standards (BS 3921:1985) *'Specification for Clay Bricks'*, which deals with dimensions, shape, strengths and water absorption, as well as durability. Manufacturers' own literature will give you the information you need.

Choosing bricklayers

Before you accept a quote from a bricklayer, do see what their work is like. Ask to see an example. Prices from bricklaying sub-contractors vary wildly, but they are often little indication as to quality.

You will also need to decide on the pointing: it makes an incredible difference as to how the finished brickwork looks. It is worth getting some technical advice – perhaps from your architect – on the weathering characteristics of different jointing profiles.

You could also look at examples of different profiles in your neighbourhood, and decide which looks the best. Perhaps the best way to choose is to get your chosen sub-contractor to knock up a few examples, using your chosen brick. Then spend a weekend deciding. The main types you will come across are:

- **Recessed pointing,** where the mortar is raked out to expose the edge of the brickwork, looks good, and shows the quality of the brick to good effect. However, such pointing may not entirely throw water running down the face of the brickwork away from the mortar joints, and the bricks may become saturated as a result. You may prefer recessed pointing on internal brickwork, for instance a fireplace, where you can enjoy the decorative advantages and not worry about whether it's raining!

- **Flush pointing** has the advantage of ensuring that the water is not retained in the joint. This is where the bottom edge of the mortar is flush with the top edge of the brick below.

- **Bucket handle pointing** leaves a concave, rounded joint.

- **Struck and weathered pointing** is where the mortar is pressed back into the brickwork at a slight angle.

Fireplace

Your bricklayers will also be responsible for your chimneys and fireplaces. An incredible amount of

21.

21. Fitting the insulation is a time-consuming task but one which cannot be avoided.

work and masonry goes into fireplaces and chimneys.

As we have already seen, a fireplace must have its own solid foundations. At ground floor level, a rectangular opening is formed to create the fireplace, with a solid concrete hearth as its base. The head of the opening is bridged with a lintel, and once the fireback is fitted a throat is installed to guide the fire's smoke up into the flue. The fireback is a fireclay insert put into the fireplace opening. Behind this, the cavity is filled with rubble or with insulating concrete.

The chimney then rises through the house to roof level and finishes with a chimney pot. The chimney may be built inside your house or as part of an exterior wall, either inside or outside the wall line.

In adjoining rooms, you can build fireplaces back to back so that their flues rise within one chimney. I have also seen a ingenious variation on this theme which is worth copying: a garden barbecue built back to back with a sitting room fireplace. The result is a weather-protected barbecue built into a chimney outside with a flue also sharing the chimney. Brilliant if you like barbecuing!

Once your bricklayers have brought the chimney through the roof, your tilers may need to return to make good the surrounding areas with stepped lead flashings – a lot depends on the siting of the chimney.

Scaffolding

It is probable that your timber frame erectors will have needed scaffolding to do their job. In this case, the scaffolding will already be on site, and you should try to get your bricklayers working as soon as possible so that the scaffolding does not stand around unused, soaking up your money.

If scaffolding has not been needed by the erectors, your bricklayers will soon need it. They will only be able to get so far before they reach this stage, and you must make prior arrangements.

A scaffolding company will usually give you a set price for hiring the scaffolding for a fixed period. After this, you normally pay by the week. Scaffolding is expensive, and your task as self build manager will be to ensure that it does not have a

22. All that remains to be done internally is to fit the plasterboard.

22.

23. Expanded metal lathing is fixed ready to receive three coats of cement render.

23.

24. Before the weathershield finish can be applied, the third and final render coat must be sponged down.

24.

25. From the outside, the house now looks almost complete. The roof has been finished, the external walls have been rendered and the feature timbers are ready for staining.

25.

prolonged stay on your site. That means calculating as accurately as possible how long the bricklayers and roofers will need it, and then making sure that these sub-contractors stick to their timescales. As your build progresses, the scaffolding will have to be lifted. Depending on your house style, and whether there are gables and chimney stacks to build, you can expect three or four 'lifts'.

Each time a 'lift' is needed, your bricklayer will tell you. It is important that he tells you in enough time for you to organise the scaffolders to come and do it. Otherwise, time will be wasted.

- If heavy rain is forecast, get the scaffolding boards turned on their sides so that dirty splashes of wet mud and mortar can't be thrown up against the house and stain the brickwork.

- Respect your scaffolding: don't let the kids play on it, and make hard hats an absolute rule.

Guttering

Until you come to build a house of your own, you don't give guttering a second glance. Now, you become totally obsessed by it, and your eyes are permanently fixed on other people's rainwater systems!

Once again, your vocabulary will change: what on earth is the fascia? Answer: it is the board that hides the ends of your roof trusses, and carries the guttering. The more pressing question, however, is: who will do your guttering?

Usually, it's a job for the plumber, a general handyman or a guttering specialist. You may even want to tackle it yourself. The important thing is that it is done while the scaffolding is still up. It is basically a question of fixing gutter runs, held up by brackets, and down pipes, which will carry rainwater into your surface water drains.

There are various rainwater systems around made in different materials: cast iron and copper are the most expensive, but they do look terrific. Most of us settle for aluminium or plastic. The guttering specialists will probably try to convince you that uPVC is the best buy, and it is certainly very low maintenance, although the initial outlay is considerable.

26.

26. The finished new home looks very smart and ready for immediate occupancy!

Chapter 13: It's decision time!

This is an important chapter. Most of the points it raises should have been decided by you at an early planning stage. If not, several important decisions need to be made and implemented now.

They include:

• **Central vacuum cleaning systems**

• **Heating, including heat recovery systems**

• **Insulation**

Built-in vacuuming

Built-in vacuum cleaning systems are very easily installed at the initial construction stage, but they are much harder to put in retrospectively. The basic installation is done at first fix stage, before the plasterboard walls are put up, and it is completed at second fix stage – all without upheaval and at very little extra fitting cost. The job can be done by a specialist installer, but it's easy enough for DIY.

A central vacuum cleaning system is usually believed to be an investment that will add to the value of your home. And there is a school of thought which suggests that one day, built-in vacuum cleaning systems will be just as standard as central heating in our homes.

The actual power unit of the system can be permanently installed wherever you want it – the garage or utility room, under the stairs, or in a basement or outside lobby. Cleaning is simply started by plugging the flexible hose into one of the vacuum outlets, fitted at pre-planned strategic points around the home. It is these that you need to fit now, so that the wiring can be installed in the walls before the plasterboard is nailed.

It is not necessary to have a vacuum outlet in every room. For a house of 1,500 square feet, two outlets downstairs and one upstairs will be perfectly adequate.

Prices of central systems vary, but for around £450 you should be able to buy a model sufficient for an ordinary-sized family house. For a model suitable for a larger house, you would have to pay more, probably around £650. On top of this, you may have to pay for the hose and cleaning attachments. And if you cannot put in the system yourself, there may also be installation costs.

Heating

How are you going to heat your new home? One assumes that you have already decided whether to have mains gas, electricity, oil, LPG, or solid fuel, and chosen between a traditional 'wet' system with wall hung radiators, underfloor heating, skirting heating, warm air, or an electric heating system. Your choice will already have had repercussions at first fix stage, although there may still be an element of choice. When we were building our house, we had always envisaged having oil fired central heating, and the first fix was laid accordingly. We subsequently opted for an Liquefied Petroleum Gas system: luckily, the first fix work was identical for both.

A timber frame house has high levels of insulation and will simply not require huge inputs of heat. Indeed, this is the trend for all new housing in the UK. The latest proposed amendments to Building Regulations will make double glazing and certain standards of insulation compulsory, so that heating systems can be chosen on grounds of sheer efficiency.

You will therefore be able to reap all the benefits of the latest technology, and can consider installing smaller but ultra-efficient heating systems. There are several interesting options in this low energy, high comfort equation, including underfloor heating and skirting heating, both of which can be powered by oil, gas, LPG or electricity. But first, a look at floor insulation. Should you or shouldn't you insulate beneath your floors?

Floor insulation

One requirement with underfloor heating is floor insulation. You can insulate your floors regardless of your type of central heating, but if you choose underfloor heating, then floor insulation is a must.

But aren't you obliged to insulate your floors anyway? Current Building Regulations (June 1991) require ground floors of new buildings to be insulated if, according to a laid down formula for calculation, they lose more than a set amount of heat. However, the vast number of new homes – probably 99.9 per cent – are completely unaffected by this Building Regulations requirement.

This could be for one of two reasons:

- The house is too big. If the total ground area of a property is larger than 15 square metres, under Building Regulations it will not require insulation.

This is because the greater the floor area, the less the proportionate heat loss, due to the fact that most heat loss at floor level is round the edges, not in the middle. It follows that the smaller the house, the greater the insulation required.

A small detached house would require about 50mm (two inches) of floor insulation; a larger detached house would require 25mm.

- If your house is exceptionally well insulated elsewhere (in other words, over-insulated by Building Regulations standards), the need for floor insulation is traded off.

In practice, if your home is double glazed and does not have exceptionally large window areas, you can forget about the requirement to insulate floors. It wil not be mandatory. You need do it only if you wish.

It is nevertheless strongly advised for a timber frame home. An uninsulated floor in a highly insulated house could theoretically cause surface condensation on the floors, particularly around the perimeters, and under carpets.

Insulation under the floor, whether it is screeded or of the suspended type, will prevent this, and will also conserve energy. But the main point of floor insulation is simply to complete the insulation equation. The inclusion of a 25mm thick expanded polystyrene insulation over the whole floor area will give you an up to 13 per cent saving in heating bills. It will also add little cost to a self build: perhaps £100 for materials for a 1,500 square foot house.

If you are having underfloor heating, the pipes for it would be laid on top of the insulation.

Underfloor heating

An underfloor central heating system is a 'wet' system, but instead of hot water passing through wall-hung radiators, it is circulated through pipes under the floor. Underfloor heating systems can be laid into any type of floor, whether screeded, floating or a suspended timber floor, and are (or should be) compatible with any type of central heating boiler.

The main advantage is that this is an 'invisible' system. There are no radiators cluttering up walls. Although underfloor heating systems are relatively expensive to install, they work at low temperatures, are more energy efficient, and so running costs are claimed to be lower – up to 25 per cent less than radiators, or so it is claimed.

Underfloor heating will give you warm floors (a definite plus in a bathroom), and will deal with condensation in rooms like conservatories and anywhere with high ceilings, because the heat is radiated from the floor so that the temperature differential between floor and ceiling is no more than two or three degrees C.

There are various systems on the market. Some consist of a semi rigid plastic pipe, heated by warm water; or there are single pipe systems of various sizes. One system consists of a triple rubber tube with a contra-flow system, which allows warm water to travel in both directions. Some manufacturers do seminars, both for installers and self builders, where more can be learned about the various systems – and where reassurance is offered that these systems do not burst or leak!

Find out what you can about each system on the market. In particular, it's worth asking:

- **Is the system compatible with standard plumbing and insulation materials, as well as with any type of central heating boiler?**
- **Does the pipe have BBA certification or a BSI kite mark?**
- **At what stage can the underfloor heating system be fitted to the first floor? This is an absolutely key point in timber frame construction, because it may delay the laying of the first floor decking. Some systems, however, can be fitted from underneath, after the decking has been laid and before the ceilings are fitted on the ground floor.**

Skirting heating

Skirting heating has similar benefits to underfloor heating, in that it is 'invisible', and frees walls for furniture, not radiators. It also spreads the same kind of uniform heat, avoiding 'cold spots' at floor level.

However, more advantages are claimed. The main one is that the system itself is easy to install and remains easily accessible. Furthermore, because it combines a skirting feature with central heating, there is no need to fix separate skirting boards; in addition, the skirting acts as a conduit for other services – electric wiring, for instance. Also, skirting heating is said to be highly responsive, in other words, quick to heat up and quick to cool down, making it even cheaper to run.

Internal Climate Control of Kingston, Surrey, is the British company which claims to have innovated skirting heating. It has installed several systems in timber frame properties, and offers two choices: one system is water borne, and can be powered by the energy source of choice; the other is direct electricity.

What sort of fuel - the burning question

Disinterested information on choosing fuel systems is difficult to get hold of (everyone wants to sell something, after all!), but looking at the Government's own figures for heating, here are the official cost comparisons for units of energy (expressed in Giga Joules):

‡ **Gas:** £4.1

‡ **Bulk LPG** (eg, Calor): £7.2

Bottled LPG: £15.9

Oil: £3.8

House coal: £3.7

Smokeless fuel: £6.0

Anthracite nuts: £4.7

Anthracite grains: £4.2

Wood: £4.1

Electricity: £19.1

‡ **Off-peak electricity** £6.7

The ‡ notes an additional standing charge. For gas, it's £37 a year, for bulk LPG £48, and for off-peak electrcity, about £12 per annum. No standing charge for peak electricity is quoted (this is £41.32), because it's assumed that electricity is used in any household, no matter how it is heated.

- **Gas** is used by 65 per cent of all households. It can run wet systems or warm air systems. It can also run tumble dryers, living flame fires, cookers, fridges and so on. There are some very impressive innovations, including condensing boilers which are ultra-efficient and also have significant environmental advantages, thermal stores and heat recovery systems. There is also a lot of flexibility in a gas heating system, including siting

of boilers. Furthermore, there is a heating design service for all houses, including specifically timber frame. Your nearest gas regional housing development manager will have details.

- **Bulk LPG** could be your choice if your preference is for gas, but you are beyond mains gas. It can be used to power exactly the same systems as mains gas, and just like mains gas, will also run living flame fires, tumble dryers, cookers and so on. You can also choose from almost exactly the same range of boilers and systems. Like gas, an LPG system must be installed by a CORGI registered installer (Council of Registered Gas Installers).

- **Oil** is the cheapest in the figures above but is prone to price fluctuations, and the boilers themselves are slightly more expensive than gas ones. At the time of writing, there is at least one oil condensing boiler on the market. Both oil and LPG are less convenient than either gas or electricity because they have to be delivered and stored in your garden, so the size of your garden, and access, are both important factors.

- **Electricity** is generally considered to be cheap to install, and provided it uses off-peak electricity, reasonable to run. Options include storage heaters; a radiator system fuelled by a boiler which runs off night electricity; and ceiling heating; you could also look at the latest systems which use heat pumps (pioneered by Creda and Flebu). The most up-to-date systems incorporate heating, ventilation, heat pumps and heat recovery in one. Different electricity companies are offering different tariff deals (for instance, off-peak electricity in afternoons as well as evenings) so it is worth inquiring. In particular, find out whether it would cost you more to use electricity at peak times if you have an off-peak metre – if it costs a couple of pence more per unit, you will have to do your sums and work out whether you will be using enough off-peak electricity to make it worthwhile.

- **Solid fuel** systems are cheap. But even with the best will in the world and automatic feed systems, there's no getting away from the fact that a certain amount of work and dust is involved.

Anyway, no one should tell you how you should heat your house because so much depends on what is available and what your lifestyle is like. The best advice is to shop around, looking at different fuels and different systems, and comparing not just installation and running costs, but also considering your own lifestyle.

The search for a perfect system can be difficult, but here are just some of the options worth considering. This is by no means a complete list (the subject is worth a whole book to itself), but is just a few ideas, very briefly described, that are interesting, efficient, and suitable for a highly insulated timber frame house.

- **Condensing boilers:** These are highly energy efficient and kinder to the environment, but are more expensive to buy than traditional gas boilers. The Government now encourages their use with grants which started in May 1993.

A condensing boiler works by extracting high levels of heat from a given quantity of gas and incorporates two heat exchangers. The first removes heat from the hot gases in the same way as a conventional boiler. The gases then pass over a second heat exchanger which removes some of the latent heat. The cooled waste gases, or condensate, are drained off.

- **Warm air central heating:** This combines heating, hot water and mechanical ventilation in one system. The diffusers are very quick and efficient; they are also very small compared with radiators. The heat recovery unit recycles heat that would otherwise be lost through ventilation, while the development of the flued heat recovery system allows the system to operate at up to 89 per cent efficiency.

- **Thermal stores:** With these systems, the domestic water service is mains-fed, so there is no need to have a tank in the loft. With no pipes that could potentially freeze up there, or take up room, this is one advantage. The other is that they are immediately responsive to demand. Hot water is pumped to radiators as required; when hot water is wanted, mains pressure cold water passes through a heat exchanger coil within the thermal store. This is so efficient that by the time it reaches the exit point, a thermostatic valve is needed to give a cold water mix. Users report that thermal stores are marvellous for showers. You do, however, need very good mains pressure for these systems; don't automatically assume that you will be able to have one in your new home.

- **Aga cookers:** An Aga not only cooks but it also provides gentle heat in the kitchen and adjoining areas. It will run on any fuel. An Aga can be connected to radiators and will also heat water. As such, an Aga could play a very useful role in an overall system. There are competitors on the market which are very well worth looking at. Stanley cookers, for instance, offer quick response cooking facilities which means not having to buy a separate cooker for the summer months.

- **Heat pumps:** These basically work like a refrigerator in reverse. They draw the temperature from one heat source (eg outgoing air) and put it in another (eg incoming air). A heating system designed with a heat pump may – or so it's claimed – save up to 30 per cent on energy bills.

- **Solar heating:** There are various ways of collecting energy from the sun, and various companies offering different systems. You need to distinguish between solar cells and solar panels. Solar panels, which are often seen on houses, harness solar heat and use it to heat water passing through pipes located inside the panels. Solar cells harness solar light, and convert sunlight into electricity. Solar panels are of limited use, because the sun is only warm for about one third of the year. Solar cells, however, use a commodity which is available every day of the year and are generally considered to be the energy source of the future.

- **Heat recovery ventilation systems:** These are reckoned to be the wind of change in modern houses! They combine thermal efficiency with the need for ventilation, and work by using damp warm air extracted from areas such as kitchen and bathroom, to pre-heat fresh incoming air. The air handling unit is usually installed in the roof space, with ductings taken to rooms below in vertical runs. The latest systems incorporate ventilation, heat recovery and heating.

Chapter 14: All gas and savings

Choosing the right central heating and hot water system for your new home is an important, early decision to make. In particular you will need to consider efficiency, controllability and, of course, running costs. You may also wish, like many of today's new home owners, to take account of environmental issues and the cumulative effects that certain domestic fuels have on global warming.

Installation costs, too, will be an obvious factor and whilst it's tempting when working within a tight budget to go for the line of least resistance, where central heating is concerned performance rather than pounds should be your ultimate criterion.

After all, you don't want to find yourself forever pouring pounds into running a cheap to install but less efficient system!

Of the main domestic heating fuels, natural gas has the reputation for being the most economical, with the additional bonus that it's also earth's friendliest fossil fuel. It emits far less carbon dioxide than does a coal-fired power station to generate the same amount of electrical energy. What's more it's available at the same economical tariff wherever you use it.

Modern gas central heating and hot water systems designed by specialist appliance manufacturers in conjunction with British Gas provide high comfort levels, quickly and efficiently, at surprisingly low running costs especially in new properties built to today's insulation levels. Traditional systems based on highly efficient appliances such as condensing and combi boilers of the type mentioned in Chapter 13 can be designed, and installed by a CORGI Registered Gas Installer, to suit every situation.

Gas central heating boilers can be floor standing or wall mounted and one example of the latter is probably the world's smallest boiler measuring only 460mm high by 300mm wide by 215mm deep. This means it will fit comfortably out-of-the-way within a standard kitchen wall cabinet but can deliver a whacking 11.7kW output capable of supplying hot water and heating to the majority of house sizes and types.

Gas warm air systems are enjoying a significant renaissance and are well worth very serious consideration. Not only do they provide economical warmth in winter, they can also produce a welcome ventilation facility when things get really sticky in the summer. In addition the option of electronic filtration is a real benefit for comfort.

The latest in this field is flued heat recovery which basically uses hot flue gases from the air heater which are mixed with warm stale air taken from the kitchen or bathroom, the heat is then extracted via a heat exchanger. On the other side of the heat exchanger, incoming fresh air is warmed and distributed to living areas. Of course, stale air and fresh air are kept separate at all times.

The beauty with this type of system is that the warm air ducts are concealed in floors or ceilings, eliminating the need for radiators. Warm air systems can also provide the domestic hot water, as well as heat a towel rail and maybe one or two radiators.

Ultimately, the efficiency and running costs of the gas central heating system you choose, go hand in glove with the control used to provide the hourly, daily, weekly operating programme. There are somewhere in the region of 100 controls from the very basic manual on-off method to state of the art devices, which can almost predict the temperature that you find comfortable. But all of them are designed with ease of use in mind.

Thermostatic radiator valves are probably the simplest way to control individual room temperatures. At the other end of the scale however, there are 24-hour and seven day electronic time switches with two outputs where central heating and domestic hot water are required at different times of the day.

In fact, unlike electricity you could have your gas central heating going on and off as many times as suits your comfort level, but clearly the ability to match your exact heating requirements reduces wasted heat and provides greater efficiency and lower running costs.

This is highlighted by the National Energy Foundation's National Home Energy Rating scheme which rates houses on a one to ten scale of energy efficiency based on such factors as heating controls, fuel type and heating system, plus good standards of insulation. For instance an old house with poor insulation and a basic electric heating system may only attain 1 or 2, whereas a modern self-built home with insulation to Building Regulations standards plus a gas central heating system and cooking by gas can probably expect to achieve an NHER of 9 and, sometimes, 10 out of 10. Many new homes with gas condensing boilers frequently gain maximum ratings.

Ultimately the choice of central heating system is in the self builder's own court, but it is an element of the complete house package which needs particular attention. Because once the house is built there are still running costs to be met. Economical gas central heating is a solution to this which also adds value to a property and is a positive selling point when you want to move to pastures new!

You can find out more about the wide range of gas central heating and hot water systems by contacting your British Gas Customer Service department whose telephone number (not the emergency number) appears under 'Gas' in your local directory. They are available between normal office hours.

Chapter 15: In a fix!

First fix is a term which the novice self builder will probably never have come across before, so here is a quick word of explanation.

Plumbing, electrics and joinery all have two stages of work in a new house. The first stage is when the basics are fixed; at the second stage or fix, the final fittings are installed.

Plumbing

First fix plumbing is one of the most crucial stages in house construction. It is not merely a question of laying pipes; it is also a matter of very careful planning.

You need to decide now on heating and water systems for your house. For the purposes of this chapter, I am assuming that your plumber will also be your heating engineer. If this is not the case, it is vital that these two co-ordinate their work, and that the one understands the work of the other.

First fix plumbing is where all the pipes that are going to be needed for the bathrooms, kitchen, cloakroom, utility and every single radiator are put in place. These pipes will be laid in the floors and will run up the walls, and will then be brought out to the desired position.

Your plumber will also put in the stack pipe, which acts as the all-important 'lung' of your house. A stack pipe runs from the top of your house to the bottom. At the top, just above roof level, air is sucked into it to keep the stack ventilated. Individual pipes from loos and basins all run into the stack, which discharges into a drain at the bottom of the house.

If you are having underfloor heating, then the piping for it should be laid now. It will probably be installed by the supplier rather than by a plumber. The pipes will radiate out over the ground floor to cover every single room, returning to a single manifold – a building term for a pipe with several outlets. The system will then be extended upstairs, via a single pipe hidden in the wall, and will again radiate out over the first floor area from a manifold.

If you are having a wet heating system, you will need to work out where the radiators will go, and what size they should be. In a timber frame house, with very high thermal efficiency, the whole object is to invest in insulation rather than heating. If you have done this, then you will not need to over-radiate. You should be able to aim for fewer and smaller radiators – and therefore more free wall space.

It is, however, important to get it right, and your plumber will be able to compute what is needed from your floor plans Make sure that your plumber/heating engineer fully understands the superior insulation levels of your timber frame house and that he downsizes your boiler and radiators accordingly. Many plumbers use a standard calculation which takes no account of insulation levels that are better than Building Regulation minimums. So be very firm about this, and if necessary, ask your timber frame manufacturer to check for you. When you are managing your own build, your job is to ensure that you have:

- **Enough radiators, but not too many**

- **Radiators in the right places**

- **Plumbing laid on in the right place for the Aga, sinks, vanity units, washing machines, etc.**

- **A system that suits your needs and which is fully planned out**

- **One question for you to decide now is whether you should have a water tank in your loft. If so, it should be installed now, before the ceilings are plasterboarded and the trap door to the loft installed.**

High pressure unvented systems have a lot going for them. Their main advantage is that all water storage and pipework is kept out of the loft, which in turn reduces plumbing work but you must have reliable, continuously adequate mains pressure.

Balanced hot and cold mains water pressure throughout the house will make life easier for you later on, if you want power showers or any of the latest high-tech appliances. Look at both unvented and thermal store systems, and learn as much as you can about them. The main differences between them are:

- Unvented systems are more powerful, but they need safety controls (which are usually factory-fitted), and your installer needs specialised training (and a certificate to show his competence).

- The latest unvented systems replace the external expansion vessel with a self-regenerating air space inside the cylinder, so that the whole installation is neater, more compact and leaves more space free in the airing cupboard.

- Thermal store systems work by mains pressure water being heated in a pipework coil passing through a hot-water cylinder. Because they are vented, they avoid the need for specialised safety controls and installer training. Although less powerful than unvented systems, their hot-water flow-rates can still be more than adequate. Thermal store technology is still being developed, with the backing of British Gas.

It is essential that the plumber who does your first fix is also around to do your second fix. Getting a second plumber in when he hasn't a clue where the pipes were laid, or how they were laid, is very difficult. So, in hiring a plumber, think long-term and try the one who is committed to carrying the job all the way through.

Ask for information about his previous installations; ensure that he guarantees his work

and ask if he will maintain and service the system in years to come. Remember that if he is going to be installing gas or LPG, he must be a registered CORGI installer.

Plumbing has changed, and continues to change, fast. If you want an up-to-date, energy efficient system, it's very important that your plumber really does know his stuff about condensing boilers, the latest radiators, and other systems. Will he be using the classic copper piping? Or the newer flexible piping? It is important that the quality of his workmanship is good, because nothing is more irritating than creaks as pipework expands and contracts across joists. Make certain that felt or some other kind of padding is put round every pipe as it lies in every notch. Your plumber should also be a perfectionist.

Another job that plumbers sometimes do is to lay the lead flashing - around the chimneys, under windows, and anywhere else where you need to seal a join. Our plumber took a real pride in the quality of his flashing – and we rewarded him by calling him Flasher!

First fix joinery

In a brick and block house, the first fix joinery would be carried out at this point. It would involve internal studwork, door linings, window boards and chipboard flooring; the loft hatch; and fixing the stairs.

A timber frame house is very different, since it is basically, a joinery package which arrives in two or three 'drops'. Manufacturers differ markedly as to what arrives when, and so a first fix in timber frame is actually quite hard to quantify. By and large, you can expect window and external door frames to be supplied and/or fitted now, with the internal doors and staircase to be supplied as part of the second fix. In comparing different packages, I find that no one seems to know whether the loft trap door is part of a first fix or a second fix!

The first fix package is usually fitted immediately after the timber frame has gone up – one of the team, for instance, may be seeing to it while his mates are fixing the roof trusses. Alternatively, the first fix items arrive on a supply only basis, for you or your own carpenter to fix.

Electrics

The first fix electrics is, like plumbing, a question of setting up the system. It is a question of planning for the future.

Again, always hire an electrician who will do both your first and second fix. The first fix electrics basically consists of working out what you will eventually need in the way of switches and sockets, and putting the wiring in place in the walls and ceilings.

Your job is to decide now what you need and where; the electrician's is to install all the necessary circuits and wiring, and to work out the most sensible and economic routes.

The major implication with timber frame is ease of installation. In masonry construction, junction boxes are fitted at first fix stage, and installed into the blockwork. With studwork walls, special plasterboard boxes are fitted at second fix, and simply slotted into holes in the plasterboard. The advantage with timber frame is that every single bit of wire and cable will go behind the plasterboard – no worries about whether to plaster it over, or hide it with PVC channelling.

Walk round your house, mentally switching lights on and off. Where do you want the lights? Where would you find it most convenient to have the switches? Where will you need two-way switching?

Lighting falls into three categories:

• **Task lighting**

• **Accent lighting**

• **General lighting**

• **Task lighting** allows you to see what you are doing. Rooms where you would need task lighting include the kitchen, where you need lights over worktops; study (work out where your desk will go); bathroom (for shaving); bedrooms (over vanity units, dressing tables, and reading lights over beds); dining or breakfast rooms and areas, where you need to see what you are eating and might want a pendant light over the table. Task lighting also includes the insides of cupboards and wardrobes, loft and (in Scandinavian houses) a semi-basement which is often called a 'crawl' space.

• **Accent lighting** is to highlight parts of rooms – you may wish to install it over pictures, for instance, and in decorative niches. Work out where you will be hanging the family portraits

• **General lighting** is the main lighting in your home. The days of one central pendant light in the sitting room, and fluorescent tubes in the kitchen, are over, and working out lighting has become altogether more complex with the trend for a much more subtle effect.

Checklist

As well as lighting, work out your other electrical requirements. Tick them off on a checklist for each room:

• **Kitchen appliances (fridge, cooker, dishwasher, microwave, etc)**

• **Utility room (boiler, washing machine, tumble drier, freezer)**

• **Garage/workshop**

• **Airing cupboard (immersion heater)**

• **Hall (doorbell)**

• **Bathroom (shaving sockets)**

• **Television/fm points**

• **Computer points**

• **Telephone/fax points**

When your house is only a shell, it is difficult to envisage how it will finally look when completely finished and fitted. But for the sake of the future liveability of your home, it is important to work out all the finer details now. The golden rule is to over-provide; if in doubt, arrange another double socket!

At the end of first fix, your house will look as though it is full of spaghetti, festooned with wiring, and with plumbing pipes in glorious abundance.

Notching, matching and drilling

Make sure that your timber frame supplier gives you details which show where notching and drilling for pipes and cables is acceptable. Then issue a copy of this to your plumber and electrician with dire warnings (like no sugar in their tea) of what will happen if they do not comply. Then check the work yourself.

Chapter 16: Windows, walls and floors

One job which is very important is sealing your house from the elements by glazing. It is possible that your frame has arrived with ready-glazed windows already fitted in the wall panels. If not, you will have to fit glazing into the construction sequence, and you can then stop worrying about the weather. It may not be possible to arrange glazing until after the second joinery fix. Don't worry! Just make sure the weather can't get in.

The main points to remember are:

- **Get at least three quotes – double glazing is a notoriously competitive business – and ask your timber frame supplier for a glazing schedule if you haven't already received one.**

- **The standard of glazing should enhance your insulation even more. Aim for triple glazing, or double glazed sealed units, preferably with low-emissivity glass. This is glass with a nearly invisible metal film on it, which reflects room heat back into the room, thus bringing double glazing up to the standard of triple glazing.**

Actually glazing your house will probably take less than a day. Inspect the work carefully and comprehensively before paying.

After your windows are glazed, you will now have a job to do yourself: you need to seal right round the edges of the frames with mastic. This comes in tubes with nozzles, and you need to push the mastic into the joints between the brickwork and your window frames. Putting mastic in the windows usually ends up being a job for the self builder because it's one that none of your sub-contractors will lay claim to, unless you have one who is pleased to do anything in the handyman line.

Insulation

It's now time to move inside, and attend to the insulation of your walls and loft. This insulation goes behind the plasterboard. It will be tucked in and around the structural timber frame, and will back on to the sheathing board. When the insulation has all been fitted in, a thick polythene vapour barrier will be installed in front of it, to prevent condensation from inside the house crossing over to the timber frame itself.

How thick will your insulation need to be? This is a key point for anyone buying a timber frame, because one of the whole objects of this method of construction is that it gives you a highly insulated, energy efficient house. Your aim should be to make the most of this: invest in insulation first, then in heating.

Some manufacturers supply insulation as part of the package; others specify it; always consider whether what is supplied or specified is sufficient, and whether it can be enhanced. The standard is 125mm insulation for the loft, and 90mm insulation for external walls and internal walls round bathrooms and loos - that's roughly five inches and three and a half inches respectively. There is no reason why you shouldn't improve on this.

The loft could have 150mm (six inches), 180mm (seven inches) or even 200mm (eight inches) of insulation laid without any trouble (beyond a little more damage to your pocket). If you wanted improved wall insulation, you would have to talk to your supplier about how to achieve this. You can't simply stuff more insulation into your walls. Medina Gimson are one package company who offer an energy enhancement option. With this, their external wall panels are 38 by 140mm studs (as opposed to the standard 38 by 89mm), which gives room for wall insulation to be increased to 140mm (five and a half inches).

U Values are:

External walls with 90mm of insulation: U-value 0.39 wm2/k

External walls with 140mm of insulation: U-value 0.28 wm2/k

Loft insulation with 150mm of insulation: U-value 0.25 wm2/k

Loft insulation with 200mm of insulation: U-valve 0.19 wm2/k

A U-value is the ratio at which an element of construction loses heat. It is expressed in watts per metre square, per degree celcius. As in golf, the lower the score the better.

Border Oak homes, with their different timber frame construction, use 90mm Styrofoam infill panels, with a U-value of 0.275. (Of course, with a Border Oak house, the insulation is integral, and you do not need to line your walls with a quilt of insulation.)

Putting up plasterboard. This particular product is Fermacell, which is a mixture of gypsum and cellulose. New to the UK, it has several advantages over most plasterboard, with easy jointing.

American homes score well in the U-value stakes. Pacific Wood say that their four and a half inch thick walls, with their inner thermal layer of insulation, produce a U-value of 0.31.

Scandinavian houses offer exceptional insulation. Nordland Homes, for instance, have 245mm (nearly ten inches) in the loft, 170mm (nearly seven inches) in the external walls, 70mm on solid ground floors, and 45mm in intermediate floors. On top of this, their windows are triple glazed and their external doors are insulated and reinforced with integral steel sheets. U-values are (Nordland's own figures): 0.11 wm2/k for the ceiling, 1.8 wm2/k for windows, and 0.23 wm2/k for external walls and ground floor. Markbohus, another Scandinavian company, pack their entire frames with eight inches of insulation. At such high levels of insulation, you are talking about relatively small heat input. In a Spaceframe system, where passive heating aims to make central heating redundant, external walls have a double framework which is 450mm (18 inches) thick. Stuffed with insulation, the U-value is 0.11 wm2/k.

You may perhaps be saying to yourself that such very thick walls and lavish thicknesses of insulation are well over the top, given the (normally) mild English climate. It's entirely for you to decide. The principles to bear in mind are:

- **Invest in insulation. It is cheap and always worthwhile.**

- **Invest up to the limits that your frame allows.**

- **The lower your U-value, the greater the energy efficiency.**

- **You only have one opportunity to do this cost-effectively.**

As for the actual business of putting in the wall insulation, this is something you may wish to do yourself. If it is not supplied as part of the package, there will probably be a recommendation. Mineral wool is normally used. It comes in rolls which are simply unrolled to fit along walls and between the trusses in the loft. Avoid burying electric cables, and wear a mask and gloves. You may find that your dryliner will do your insulating and then fix the vapour check over.

A vapour check is either a polythene sheet, nailed to the studs, or it is the backing on the plasterboard.

Plasterboarding

A timber frame house is drylined throughout. This involves lining all the internal walls and ceilings with plasterboard. This is quite often seen as a DIY job by a self builder, although it is not a particulary easy task. Plasterboard is heavy and cumbersome stuff. However, if you do decide to have a go, good luck – just don't get divorced over it!

Drylining is done in two stages and usually by two different 'trades': first, the plasterboard is tacked up; secondly, it is taped and jointed, so that all the joins and nails are invisible, and the plasterboard appears as a smooth, continuous run of wall. The real art of drylining is the jointing. Sadly, I have seen beautiful houses let down by bumpy ceilings and uneven walls, so make sure you get someone really good whose previous work you can inspect.

There is another option to having the boards joined. Here the plasterboard receives a skim (or a very thin coat) of plaster. This gives the wall a rather more traditional and solid feel which appeals to some people; others may feel that one of the points of timber frame is that it's a dry construction.

The other major point about plasterboard is the sheer amount of time it saves. What can be achieved in a matter of hours using sheets of plasterboard would take a traditional wet plasterer days.

There are various sorts of plasterboard, available in different sizes, and it's worth discussing with your dryliner first what is best. In particular, have a look at the newest types, fibre reinforced gypsum panels. These are easy to install, have a good finish which requires very little jointing, and are very strong: they cope well with knocks and abrasions, and can take shelves or other equipment as securely as a solid wall – in other words, without rupturing and with less need for noggings.

Commonly, plasterboard has one grey side and one ivory side, and comes in different sheet sizes, usually 2.4m by 1.2 m (eight by four feet). It comes in two thicknesses, 9.5mm and 12.7mm, or three-eighths and half an inch respectively.

It is also available with a waterproof membrane or thermal insulation bonded on to the back; treated to make it more moisture resistant and more fire resistant; and with square edges or tapered edges on its long sides. For a painted or wallpapered finish, you need tapered edge boards, fixed with the long edge in line and then jointed.

If you are going to finish the plasterboard with a plaster skin or other textured finish, you will need to square edge boards with the joins staggered. In both cases, the ivory side of the board is kept facing out, ie towards you.

Plasterboard is easy to cut and shape with a sharp knife and a straight edge. It is fixed with 4cm plasterboard nails (galvanised to prevent staining) at 15cm intervals. Make sure each board is firm against its backing, and that the nail itself is driven all the way home. There should be no give in the board. The boards are best fixed with their long edges vertical; just occasionally, it's considered better to fix them horizontally instead.

Fixing plasterboard on ceilings is a two-person job. If your plasterboarder is working on his own, you could offer your labour here. If you are doing it yourself, you will need the services of a friend or spouse; alternatively, a panel lifter can be hired to support the boards while they are nailed in place to the ceiling joists.

The main points to remember are:

- **For the walls, don't forget the electrics: neat rectangular holes should be cut in the plasterboard and cable ends pulled out.**

- **When the plasterboard arrives, store it in a dry place and on a flat surface. If the moisture content gets too high, the board will be virtually useless; don't over-stack – it bends the boards.**

- **Co-ordinate the taping and jointing so that it follows closely on the heels of the plasterboard erecting – a day or two's start may well be all that's needed.**

- **Ensure you can call your dryliner back, if necessary, to clear up any problems (the correct phrase is 'make good') after the second fix trades have finished.**

Screeding

It is now time to screed the floor - if that is your chosen finish. It may not always be necessary or your preference, or indicated by the timber frame supplier. A screed is a mixture of sand and cement, laid to make a very smooth floor surface on top of which you can lay carpets, tiles, linoleum or whatever you want.

All the pipes – for bathrooms, central heating, etc. – that were laid at first fix will now be buried in this screed. It is an extremely good idea for future reference to know exactly what is where, just in case a leak develops or you want to get at the pipes for any other reason. So before the screed is laid, make detailed notes or sketches; better still, take photographs or even, as some people do, use a camcorder. Then keep all these in the records of your self build. Hopefully, you will never need to look at them!

Chapter 17: Finishing off

It is now time for the second, or final fix which will give your new house heat, light and a finished appearance. Just as with your first fix, there is no reason why your second fix electrics, plumbing and joinery work should not all be carried out at the same time. You could also arrange for external decoration to be under way simultaneously.

This really is the most efficient way of organising the penultimate stage of your build. It obviates delay, and it also ensures that your plumbing and electrical sub-contractors are on site at the same time, working together. Their teamwork is very important, because much of their work goes hand in hand.

Once the second fix has been completed, the very final stage will then consist of fitting and tiling the kitchen and utility room, tiling elsewhere and then doing all the internal decoration.

It's easy to fall frustratingly behind schedule as your house nears completion, so start planning your timetable well in advance to ensure that all your sub-contractors are on site when you need them, with all materials ordered, and – most important of all – that you won't have a financial hiccough holding everything up.

As soon as the drylining is completed, you should move straight on to:

Penultimate stage:

- External decoration (can start a little earlier)
- Second fix joinery
- Second fix plumbing } to be carried out simultaneously
- Second fix electrics
- External works (landscaping, tidying up)

As you will have so many 'trades' on site, you may well decide that this would be a very good time to make yourself as available as possible to manage everything that's going on. This is also very much the stage of the build when even if you have done no DIY of any description until this moment, you might feel impelled to join in!

When the second fix sub-contractors have finished, you must organise the last part of the whole project.

Final stage:

- Internal decoration
- Kitchen (and utility) to be fitted
- Tiling of all walls to be carried out
- Flooring (carpets, floor tiles, etc.)
- Final external works (laying patio, etc)

These tasks can be carried out in swift succession and, to some degree, simultaneously. How long this final stage takes depends partly on the size of your house, and partly on the degree to which you are able to co-ordinate everything.

Second fix joinery

It is another red letter day for the self builder of a timber frame home when the second fix joiners start work.

The second fix joinery items usually include: internal doors, architraves, skirtings, loft trap, slatted shelves for airing cupboards, wardrobe fronts, garage doors, and – most important of all – the staircase.

A Scandinavian kit house goes up.

1. Day 1 - trailer arrives on site direct from Sweden.

2. Day 1 - the external wall panels are erected.

1.

2.

There is a tremendous amount of variation in the second fix package with (usually) an element of pick and choose. You may, for instance, wish to get all your own doors and wardrobes. There is also the question of who does the second fix joinery – a good local carpenter of your own choice, or a team recommended by the timber frame supplier. It would be worth comparing prices and, just as importantly, projected time scales.

A joinery second fix does not seem to be on the same scale as erecting timber frame. In fact, it is twice as complicated and fiddly, and you can expect it to take twice as long even in the hands of a skilled practitioner.

Second fix plumbing

This is really when you begin to feel that the finish is in sight. The first fix plumbing left various pipes sticking up, but nothing on the ends of them. The second fix plumbing will attach the boiler and radiators for a wet plumbing system, loos, baths and basins. Once again, as with the first fix, the assumption is that your plumber is also your heating engineer. If you are having a mains gas or LPG system, remember that your installer must be

CORGI registered.

Your heating system will have been planned before this stage, although you will still have to choose and buy radiators, the actual boiler itself, and any gas fires.

You will also be busy shopping around for bathroom suites, loos and vanity units. The choices seem endless, and even though the current fashion is for classic white sanitary ware, there is still a surprising amount of variety. It is at this stage that you will probably see how well you have managed to control your budget. If the contingency has been eaten up and there has been any overspend, you will have to downgrade your ideas about luxurious bathrooms.

If your contingency is still intact, you can splash out!

If you plan to buy a water filter, water softener, power shower, whirlpool bath, or just fancy taps, discuss the implications with your plumber (and very often with your electrician) and make sure that all these items are correctly fitted.

Water filters are worth considering for anyone worried about their drinking water. They need to

3. Day 2 - the triple glazed windows are already fitted in their respective wall panels.

3.

be connected to the main. Water from the main travels to the tap via the filter. Systems vary from the very simple to the sophisticated, and costs vary accordingly.

Water softeners are usually installed in the utility, kitchen or loft. They are definitely worth considering if yours is a hard water area and you want to avoid limescale damage to pipes and appliances. Hard water can cost you over £200 a year in extra fuel and detergent. Government research has shown that just quarter of an inch of limescale in a heating system reduces energy efficiency by 40 per cent.

Water softeners cost from around £400 to £1,000, and installation will cost around £100. Running costs add up to around £30 a year for salt, and about £2 in electricity annually. A separate tap for unsoftened drinking water is recommended, and this can be connected via a water filter.

Much cheaper are magnetic descalers, marketed as alternatives to water softeners and claimed by manufacturers to stop scale and fur forming. These cost from around £40 to £380, and cost about £2 a year in electricity to run.

Bathrooms get more hi-tech by the week. But don't go crazy and buy something glamorous and sophisticated without first checking about what kind of plumbing it will need:

- **Taps:** Single-lever bathroom mixers sound so simple, but need balanced water pressure. It's also a good idea to install a safety device, which can be set to guard against scalding. It works by limiting the lever's movement on the hot side. If your overall plumbing scheme involves unbalanced bathroom water pressures, forget single-lever mixers and go for ordinary taps.

- **Showers:** The latest are computerised. One model will even sense the mixed water temperature 200 times a second and adjust it accordingly. Or it can be used to fill a bath to a pre-set temperature and depth. Electronic touchpad controls are augmented by special plumbing arrangements. Power showers come in several different forms and they are available at varying prices. You can also get power bathrooms where hot and cold water is mixed and distributed to bath, shower and basin. The advantages are a safety check against scalding and good hot water economy.

4. Day 3 - the gable head walls are assembled and erected.

- If you are feeling really sophisticated, you can have **a shower enclosure** that also offers steam and aromatherapy! This is pure luxury, but it also has a plumbing implication. The same applies to whirlpool and spa baths. Don't go out and buy these, or any other similarly glamorous options, without first making sure that you have designed a plumbing system that can cope.

It is very important that you are satisfied that every part of your plumbing and heating system works before you finally pay off your sub-contractor. The whole system should be tested thoroughly first.

Ensure, to your own satisfaction, that nothing leaks or creaks; that all radiators are uniformly hot; that zoned systems work. British Gas will, in any case, test for leaks in your system when they connect up your supply.

Second fix electrics

Your electrical system will also need to be tested before your local electricity company will agree to connect it up. Your electrician will arrange this; make sure that this testing is part of the quote for the second fix.

The electrical second fix is to install lighting

throughout, and to put in all the sockets. Be prepared in a timber frame house for some heart-stopping moments, as the electrician cuts holes into your precious new plasterboard to install boxes for sockets and switches. In the kitchen, if you have eyeball lighting, he may cut similarly unsightly holes.

Do not worry! Something that no one has told you about until right now is that your dryliner will be expecting to come back and sort out any such problems. It should be a matter of just a few hours' work.

Once all the electrical circuits are in place and have been tested, the electrician will have to give the electricity board a signed test certificate. After that, the electricity board themselves will lay a cable to your meter box and connect up the system.

This process may take anything from a few days to several weeks. It is obviously important that you do not pay your electrician in full until your power supply is on and you can see for yourself that it is working according to its original designs.

Finishing post

While all this has been going on, the external

5. Day 5 - dormer construction begins.

5.

decoration may have been completed. Now the decorator – you perhaps? – can move inside to finish off: staining internal joinery, applying gloss paint, and covering walls and ceilings. Here, one of the joys of timber frame comes shining through. In a brick and block house, you would have to wait for the plasterwork to dry out before decorating. And you would probably then cautiously opt for nice safe magnolia paint, so that when cracking appeared (as it very likely would) you would not mind too much. In fact, you would probably expect to redecorate all over again in a year or two.

With a timber frame, you can choose paint, wallpaper, whatever you like, and get on with it straightaway. There will be no cracking and no damp stains; and no need to redecorate soon.

And of course there's nothing to stop you choosing magnolia paint – the difference is that you will be choosing it because you like it!

Outside

Work will undoubtedly continue for some time on tidying up, landscaping, and laying down a final drive surface. You may also have a garage to complete before you can get a completion certificate (this will be the case if the garage formed part of your planning application).

Completion

When you feel you are as finished as you need to be, you need to obtain a completion certificate. If you have an architect who has been giving you progress certificates throughout the build, he now pays one last visit and – hopefully – issues an official letter of completion. The building inspector will also want to be satisfied about completion, and may issue a certificate or letter of completion, as will the NHBC or Foundation 15 inspector if your build has been registered with those bodies. Your building society or other lender may also want to send a surveyor to check.

After completion, you have only three months in which to submit your VAT claim. Don't delay!

It's a counsel of perfection to say that you should try to ensure that all your purchases are VAT-refundable (curtain rails, for example, all tiles, outside paving). I have known people delay getting completion certificates so that they can put off re-claiming VAT, simply so that they can carry on buying such materials.

6. Days 16-20 - brickwork begins. The roof is already tiled and in place.

6.

However, although it is frustrating to miss obtaining a very nice discount on some items, you also have to be pragmatic. Sometimes, it's just very nice indeed to get that completion certificate, do your VAT sums, and start enjoying your beautiful new home.

Snags?

Of course you hope that nothing whatever will go wrong with your house.

But what happens if there are snags?

- **If your house has been built by one major contractor, then you should have agreed that within six months, you will both draw up 'snag' lists. These will be compared and agreed between you. The builder will then put them right. When you are satisfied, you will release the sum of money you originally agreed to withhold (usually two and a half per cent).**
- **Recall sub-contractors who have guaranteed their work to you in writing. This is when it pays to keep paperwork! If your sub-contractors are non-cooperative and belong to a trade body, you could ask for arbitration.**
- **Do not hesitate to go back to your timber frame supplier with any worries. Any reputable company**
will want to be given the chance to inspect and put right problems which may relate to the frame.
- **If anything major seems to be wrong and no one wishes to take responsibility, go back to your architect, surveyor or the building inspector for advice.**

The prospect of snags should not worry you unduly. The huge majority of self built timber frame homes are excellent, sound structures, generally built and finished to an extremely high standard.

And finally . . .

Please be very happy in your new home, and proud of your achievement. And if you have come to this part of the book and thought, *"Wow, I could do that!"*, then yes, you can.

Self building is a challenge, but it is not particularly difficult, and it can be done very well if you think it all through, plan accordingly and manage it efficiently. Few things are more richly satisfying to achieve or more enjoyable – as you will see from the next part of the book

7. Days 21-25 - the external brick cladding is complete.

7.

Part 4
Case studies

Self builders talk about their experiences of using timber frame for projects ranging from large standard designs, to a small one-off bungalow. We even meet one man who made his own frame.

Case study: A latter day rectory

This case study features a traditional English country-house style home. The largest in Potton's Georgian-inspired Rectory range, it recaptures that golden age - with the addition of some state-of-the-art technology, including underfloor central heating. It was built on a site that became a building plot when the planning authority agreed that an old farmhouse already there could be demolished and replaced. This self build illustrates the flexibility of timber frame, being built to a standard design that was modified to the owners' requirements. Building costs worked out to around £60 a square foot, reflecting the owners' desire for a very high standard of specification.

From the house, there is an uninterrupted view across the flat, peaceful fenlands of Cambridgeshire to Ely Cathedral, which is often regarded as the most beautiful cathedral of all.

At night, the view becomes even more spectacular when the cathedral is illuminated.

The cathedral is at least four miles away, and is almost the only building visible in this most tranquil of settings. There are no rows of houses, only the odd farm building dotting the landscape; no noisy roads, only a network of quiet lanes; the greatest activity is at harvest time.

It would be hard to imagine, let alone find, a better situation for a brand new country house.

Yet, when David and Sue Lacey first saw it, they weren't at all sure it was right for them.

The couple, with three horse-mad daughters and a menagerie of animals, had been attracted by the estate agents' particulars describing a farmhouse with four acres, in a setting well off the beaten track. The remoteness was in itself a great attraction. The couple had already self built once, but they were living too close to a main road for their liking. The property they went to see, however, had little apart from peace and space, to offer.

"When I saw it, I hated it," Sue recalls. The old farmhouse was falling down, due to settlement. Part of it originally dated back to Domesday times, but the authenticity had been lost in a 1950s extension. It was only when the couple stood away from the house, and realised that they were standing on what could be the perfect plot for a new house –

providing, of course, that they could get planning permission – that they decided they simply had to buy it. The original house, with its land, had been part of a large working farm until some ten years previously. Because of its condition, there was no problem getting planning permission for a replacement house, and the couple signed an agreement with the local authority agreeing to demolish the old house within three months of moving into the new.

They bought the property in April 1990, set about getting the planning permission, started building in the July of that year, and moved in the following May, 1991. They've been happy ever since: *"It's turned out wonderfully,"* says Sue. *"We absolutely love it here."*

David and Sue had self built a brick and block house before, but were now keen to do a timber frame property. They chose a Potton Milchester, the largest in the company's acclaimed Rectory range.

There are five houses in this range, and like any timber frame, it's possible to modify any of the designs.

The Milchester is, by any standards, a huge house, perfect for family living. Upstairs, there are four good bedrooms and a family bathroom leading off the very large landing. There is also a master suite, which can be best described as a wing. Here, there is a sitting room, a huge airing cupboard, a very large bathroom, something which is described on the plans as a 'wardrobe' but which is in fact easily big enough to have a window and use as a bedroom, and the master bedroom itself.

This wing lends itself to a number of flexible uses. For instance, it can be completely self contained and used as a granny annexe, with the alleged 'wardrobe' plumbed and turned into a kitchen.

The Laceys simply find that having an upstairs sitting room is perfect as a television room which daughters Joanne, 16, Rebecca, 13, and Katherine, 10, have adopted as their own.

Downstairs, is a superb formal sitting room with a period style wooden and marble fireplace and windows overlooking the terrace, a dining room, also with a fireplace, a study, utility room, cloakroom, farmhouse kitchen/breakfast room, and beyond that, a family room.

This glamorous country house is the largest in Potton's Georgian-inspired Rectory range. Its view out across fields towards Ely Cathedral is hard to beat.

David and Sue Lacey in their comfortable and spacious sitting room.

The handsome stone balustrade (supplied by Haddonstone) along the back of the house makes a charming feature.

The Laceys adapted their Milchester slightly. The original utility was enlarged by about eight feet, by bringing it out under a sloping roof, in line with the dining room. The extension has been ingeniously handled, with a Velux window in the enlarged roof. Sue and David wanted a large utility room: *"With three daughters, two horses, and a couple of dogs, there's always a lot of activity, and plenty of muddy boots,"* says Sue.

Their other adaptation was to the family room beyond the kitchen. In the standard Potton design, this is shown as a semi-round garden room, above which the master bedroom overhangs by perhaps two feet all round, and with pillars supporting the overhang. The Laceys felt that this arrangement was a waste of space, and opted for the room to be built out to its full dimensions.

The house is powered by Calor gas, and has an underfloor heating system, which the Laceys say took a little getting used to after a lifetime with wall-hung radiators, but which they now regard as an unqualified success.

Mains gas was not available, and David and Sue did not want to consider oil, which they felt would be noisy and smelly. The Calor gas tank sits out in the garden, almost invisible behind some screening by the garage. The Calor fuels not just the central heating system, but also the Aga in the kitchen and the three living flame gas fires in the reception rooms.

The underfloor heating system, by Wirsbo, was put in at first fix stage, on top of some tracked insulation to ensure that the heat goes up into the house, not into the ground below. On the ground floor, plastic pipes were laid in a network in each room, turning every floor into a radiator. The pipes all feed back into one manifold, in the utility room, and a single pipe feeds the system upstairs, to two manifolds upstairs. Upstairs, the plastic pipes network out into each room, just as downstairs. The installation was carried out by Wirsbo themselves, with finishing touches by the Laceys' local plumber, Bob Smith.

Having this type of central heating system did have implications during the build of the house. It meant notching out joists, where the pipes were to be laid, and also involved placing the joists more closely together on the first floor. It also meant that the erectors were not able to fit out the upstairs of the house because the heating pipes were not in place.

Twin Ideal 2 condensing boilers are wall-hung in the utility room, working in tandem to heat the house and supply the hot water. It is not always necessary to have both on, and during the summer, the Laceys can switch both off and choose to heat their water by electricity.

They also find that the Aga throws out a useful amount of heat, and because care was taken to design a really efficient system, with three different heating zones in the house, energy bills have not been nightmarish.

David Lacey says: *"I have been pleasantly surprised. In the depths of our first winter here, it was costing no more than £40 a week, and that included all our cooking, as well as hot water and heating. For much of the year, it works out at a great deal less."*

The underfloor heating system provides an effective, uniform heat throughout the house, whilst also completely freeing the walls of radiators. The build of the house was managed entirely by the Laceys themselves. They were in the fortunate position of not having to take out an overdraft and, without responsibilities to any lender, decided against using Foundation 15, NHBC or architect's certification. David, who has longstanding professional experience as a surveyor, took the view that should he ever come to sell the house (which he doesn't intend to do), the property will stand up to any survey. He is cynical about the value of some forms of certification.

During the build, all work was sub-contracted out, apart from the actual erection of the frame. The Laceys' philosophy was to use small local firms wherever possible.

It certainly paid off in their choice of Wright and Butcher, the builders responsible for most of the work apart from the actual erection of the frame. The foundations could have been tricky, as the plot is in an area of deep, sticky clay, where ground movement had caused tremendous problems in the older house on site.

David Lacey used an engineer to do a report; as a result, footings went down 1.2 metres and were filled with concrete. When the Potton erection team arrived, they were full of praise for the groundwork, and said it was the best oversite they had ever seen. There were hiccoughs during the course of the build, including the delay to finishing the first fix, caused by installing the heating system. In the end, the first fix was completed by Wright and Butcher.

There was also an irritating problem caused by the windows. Building regulations had changed, and although the new requirement was noted on the plans, the windows were somehow all supplied and installed without trickle ventilators. As a result, the building inspector refused to certify the work, and David found himself responsible for installing each window ventilation unit.

Getting services on to the site was also a complication. Although water and electricity were already there – theoretically – both systems needed renewing. For extra peace of mind, the Laceys also have a generator, which will be just enough to keep most things in the house ticking over in the event of a power cut – an important consideration in their remote, rural situation.

The property has no mains drainage, but a Klargester Bio Disc septic tank has proved an excellent investment. It is buried in the garden, virtually undetectable, apart from a small above-ground cloche.

The entire project did not work out particularly cheaply, but the Laceys always took the view that their new home should be built and finished in true country house style: *"We wanted to do it properly, with high quality fittings. In a house like this, cutting corners always shows,"* says David.

The Wilson and Glick fitted kitchen, spotted at the Ideal Home show, is in painted oak – a compromise between Sue's wish for a wooden kitchen, and David's desire for a white one. The sink is Franke. The utility room has been fitted out with units from the family's previous kitchen. The bathroom sanitary ware is all part of Armitage Shanks' plain white Cottage range, with brass taps by Adams. The Laceys consider their power showers one of their best buys.

A beautiful home in every respect, responsibility for the interior decoration lay with Sue, whose skill and sense of colour can be seen everywhere. Dado rails are used to great effect downstairs, with some superb wallcoverings and light fittings. The girls' bedrooms have been decorated with Dulux Duet, a paint effect that looks like wallpaper.

All the furniture was chosen with great care for each room, with pride of place undoubtedly going to some exquisite hand-made dining room furniture, of 12 chairs, a large table and dresser, which is the work of Dougie Phipps.

The Laceys' project did not finish with the house itself. Outside there is a triple garage, stabling for the family's two horses, and paddocks which have been professionally post and railed. The gardens have been extensively landscaped, with a large hard area outside the back door, and some truly stunning stone balustrading on the raised main terrace.

This is by Haddonstone, the company which also supplied the magnificent front porch. Visually, the house looks fittingly large and imposing, with high brick walls on either side. Altogether, no fewer than 50,000 bricks were used for the house and landscaping. The bricks used are Butterley Arlesley Gault, which at the time of the build cost £250 per 1,000. Tiles are Breckland Black, by Redland.

The total project worked out to *"the wrong side of £200,000"*, says David. This sum does not include the original cost of the old farmhouse and its four acres, so that the build itself came to around £60 a square foot, much higher than Potton's guide price.

However, as the Laceys point out, they were purposely building to the highest possible specification, and they spent out on extras, such as the brass light fittings, fitted wardrobes in all bedrooms, the outside lighting, underfloor heating, landscaping, the stone porch and balustrading, and so on.

Has it all been worth it? Undoubtedly. *"We were building for ever."* With Ely Cathedral, centuries old, the only visible landmark in the distance, that seems exactly the right reply.

Case study: Building on a shoestring

Unlike the preceding case study where the aim was a luxurious specification, the aim of this one was to keep costs down to the absolute minimum. This story shows how one young couple succeeded in self building a 1,700 square foot four bedroomed house, at around £24 a square foot, despite a number of difficulties. They managed their own build throughout, did much of the work themselves, despite no previous building experience, and kept an accurate tally of costings.

Melanie Weight was a 19-year old bride when she and her husband Andrew became self builders. They did so for one reason only – to make savings.

The Weights were early victims of the recession in housing. In 1989, as newly weds, they had wanted to buy their first home in the Reading area where they have their roots.

Housing prices in the Thames Valley were, however, astronomical until the summer of that year when the market spiralled into collapse. But by then, unable to afford a house in their chosen area, Andrew and Melanie had bought a starter home some distance away, near Southampton.

It was affordable (just!), but it involved a round trip of 140 miles every day to get to work. Within months, both were exhausted, and finding it easier to live during the week in Reading with Andrew's parents, Michael and Ann. The starter home went back on the market and before long, Melanie and Andrew were caught in the negative equity trap: its value fell so fast, that they simply couldn't afford to sell it.

They did the only thing possible, and rented it out. Then, they started house hunting again in the Reading area. Unwilling to rent, and unable to afford a bridging loan, their only solution was to self build, and this itself was only possible because the National and Provincial Building Society was then offering a special deferred mortgage scheme to self builders.

No capital was needed (which was just as well, since the Weights still had their equity tied up in the first house) and the money to buy the land and build would be advanced in five stages, with no repayments due for a year. Confident that their first property would surely have sold by then, the young

couple grasped the opportunity, seeing it as providing exactly the breathing space they needed. Finance agreed, Melanie and Andrew, set about looking for a plot. The overwhelming requirement was that it had to be cheap. Andrew telephoned every single estate agent in the Reading phone book, and found a building plot on the market at £33,000.

The plot is in Caversham Park Village, an estate just outside Reading on the Berkshire/Oxfordshire border. Built in the sixties, the original developers still retain rights over all subsequent development. Not one further house had been built since the estate was finished 30 years previously.

The plot that was for sale had been part of a larger-than-average garden. Measuring 110 feet long, with a 42 feet frontage, it had full detailed planning consent for a 1,700 square foot house with an integral garage. With hindsight, the Weights would like to have varied the consent, but at the time they lacked the nerve. However, they have altered it substantially since.

As it was, they didn't exactly hang around: *"We completed on May 27, 1990, which was a Friday, and the following Monday, we were digging holes,"* Melanie remembers.

They had borrowed £80,000 in total, of which £33,000 had gone on the plot. With a budget of only £47,000 remaining, it was important not to overspend.

Groundworks, however, proved more extensive than anyone had realised and cost more than double the original estimate because they had to dig down two metres before they could establish a level base, and disposing of 180 tonnes of soil was both difficult and expensive.

One of the happiest elements of the build, however, was the excellent relationship the Weights developed with their timber frame suppliers, Select Timber Frame. Founded in 1986, Select Timber Frame offer no designs of their own. As they say, *"More often than not, our clients give us drawings sketched on the backs of envelopes and we take it from there. We specialise in one-offs and we try to give value for money in our kits. We strongly believe in offering a personal service and we are very discerning about the materials we use. If we don't like the look of anything, we won't put it on a lorry*

The frame was swiftly erected by the Select team without using any scaffolding.

The finished frame, complete with roof trusses, is now ready to take the brick cladding.

Melanie and Andrew Weight in front of their newly completed home.

and send it on to our clients. Our approach seems to pay off. Our clients are usually our best advertisements."

Although Derek Wenn and Robin Harris, the directors of this small family company, had not designed the original house which had received the planning permission, they are well used to translating sketches, ideas and even full-scale designs originally intended for masonry construction, as was the case here.

Their service included setting out the foundations, checking the dimensions and levels of the slab, erecting the timber frame itself using family labour, and supplying glazing, doors, skirting, felt, battens and even all the nails. Nothing proved too much trouble for this small company, and help – even on a Sunday afternoon – was never more than a phone call away.

Once the slab was in place and the frame up, the brickwork was to prove a major problem. The friend who started it was unable to finish, and with two-thirds still to do, a bricklaying team had to be hired afresh.

Unfortunately, they kept changing their rates, first charging for piece work, and then for day rates. Melanie and Andrew ended up by paying them £1,100 for the work they had done, then sacking them, but the job still wasn't finished. Even worse, a ladder was left leaning against a window and some youths climbed in and stole plumbing goods and copper piping worth £800.

Finally, the brickwork was finished to a very high standard by a retired bricklayer who charged £600. Then came the roof, which Melanie and Andrew did themselves, with the help of Andrew's dad Michael. They managed it in just three weeks.

Melanie and Andrew then set about doing the whole of the second fix themselves, moving in before they were anywhere near finished. That was in October 1990. The house was weatherproof, but the plasterboarding, plumbing and electrics all needed to be done.

"We moved in with a futon to sleep on, a portable gas heater, and a camping stove. Our neighbours very kindly allowed us to run an electrical extension from their garage so that we had light. We lived on mashed potatoes, beans and pasties. And we used to go down to the local leisure centre for showers," Melanie remembers.

That autumn, the couple worked very hard on the house, and took on extra work outside to pay for it. At one stage, Melanie had a full-time job as a printer, a part-time job with the same company, and also an evening cleaning job.

Two months later, a bitter blow fell, when Andrew, a photocopy engineer, was made redundant. Unable to find a new job, he used the four months to finish off the house. He and his wife did all the wiring themselves, and Andrew put up all the plasterboard - a job he now considers to have been the hardest of the lot. The plasterboard was then finished by skimming, done by a professional plasterer. Andrew also did all the plumbing, including the central heating system, and installed the fitted kitchen.

There was a small stroke of luck when Melanie got through to the finals of a DIY competition for women, and won £250 in the finals - enough for the bathroom suite.

All the internal doors were hung and the skirting and architraves put up by Michael Weight, a carpenter, and finally Melanie and Andrew did all the decorating and tiling themselves.

Exactly one year after starting work, the house was complete, built and finished to a very high standard, barely over budget, and fully certificated by a surveyor. It was immediately valued at £129,950, having cost just over £70,000 to build (£86,000 including interest and VAT, which was later refunded).

When the house was finished, Melanie and Andrew were in a quandary as to what to do next: their first house remained unsold, and the market was continuing to fall deeper into recession.

For a time, they even moved back to their original home and rented out their self built house. Things started to resolve themselves soon after. Melanie and Andrew decided to rent out their first home permanently, to move back into their new house, and to share it with lodgers for a while, to help pay both mortgages.

Hard work, yes, but even despite the recession, it has all turned out happily. Andrew now works as a driving instructor; Melanie hopes to start her own wedding business soon. Their first house is still not worth what they paid for it, but the rent now covers their mortgage. In contrast, the self built house still has a value well in excess of what it cost to achieve.

"For a while, things did look pretty bleak, but that was because we had not managed to sell our first house, something no one could have foreseen. We are now used to the idea of renting it out," says Andrew. *"We look at ourselves and are very pleased. Not many young couples our age have achieved what we have managed."*

When they were building their house, in the middle of a large estate of brick and block houses, the method of construction attracted a lot of interest. For Andrew and Melanie, their choice of timber frame has paid off handsomely: *"The house is incredibly well insulated and as a result is very quiet and warm. It's strongly built and very economical to run."*

Since finishing the build, the couple have rearranged the internal layout, so that there are now five bedrooms. They are planning to build a detached double garage, and convert the integral space into further accommodation.

This tale of self build could easily have gone horribly wrong. Like many other young couples who bought their first home during the over-heated property boom, the Weights were sucked into a depressing state of negative equity. The mortgage arrangements they were able to make then would be impossible now - and rightly so.

Yet the fact is that because Andrew and Melanie were able to self build, they have got by very well. They point out that neither had any special skills: they simply learned as they went along because they had to, and were never afraid to ask Select Timber Frame for advice. Building timber frame was, they say, an important factor: *"It was so quick and easy,"* says Andrew. *"One day we will definitely do it again."*

Derek Wenn of Select Timber Frame, says: *"We were very impressed with what Mr and Mrs Weight did, but not surprised. Many of our clients have never been near a building site before, but it's amazing how well they cope in building their own homes."*

Costs:

Plot: £32,000

Timber frame kit (included frame, windows, double glazing, felt, batten and all nails): £22,500

Foundations: £6,000

Wiring: £500

Plumbing: £1,600

Brickwork: £2,500

Tiling: £400

Internal walls: £800

Other items took the actual cost of plot and build to just over £70,000.

With interest, the self build cost a total of £86,000, including £7,000 VAT.

Melanie Weight is a quick learner and she was soon able to carry out the roofing herself.

Case study: Family home in Kent

For the couple in this case study, David and Sue Cox, it was a case of second time round. They had already self built one house – of brick and block – in a Kent village; when they came to do it again, in a neighbouring village they opted for a timber frame kit. They bought their land at auction, and because it was a double plot, needed to buy both plots and sell one of them on the same day.

David and Sue Cox are now keen to self build a third time. If they do, David says they will once again choose a timber frame kit, probably from the same suppliers, Medina Gimson. His main reasons for preferring timber frame to brick and block are simple: speed of erection, and no drying out time. *"Timber frame gives you a weathertight shell in such a short time, compared with brick and block build. It means that you can quickly be working in the dry.*

"Having experienced both sorts of construction, I am also a firm believer in the advantages of having no wet trades involved in the build as is the case with timber frame.

"To encourage our brick and block house to dry out, I hired a de-humidifier, and moved it into each room round the house. Each morning, I was able to throw away two gallons of water. No wonder brick and block normally takes such a long time to dry. The amount of water used in construction is unbelievable. With our present house, we were able to move in as soon as we wanted, and we haven't experienced any cracks in the walls or ceilings."

The parents of grown-up children, David and Sue feel that self build is something they had been waiting to do.

David now says: *"I should have done it 25 years ago. I was always very keen on the idea, although it wasn't until we had an extension done at a previous home and the bricklayer said that I could have done it myself, that we felt really inspired."*

The first self build, however, that the Coxes tackled got off to a difficult start.

Having bought a plot of land with planning permission, they then employed an architect to come up with a detailed design and supervise the build. Although the Coxes liked his design well enough, when the architect put it out to tender, the cost came in at one and a half times their budget.

Having paid the architect £4,500, David and Sue then had to dispense with his services and go ahead on their own. Looking back on it, says David, the architect did them a favour. By managing their own build, employing their own sub-contractors and buying their own materials, the couple managed to bring the entire build under budget.

The family lived happily in that house, but David now had the bit between his teeth: *"Having done it once, we wanted to do it again, and this time get everything right,"* he says.

They were able to take advantage of the then roaring housing market, and sell their first house well - enabling them to be mortgage-free for their second build. They were, however, as they point out, selling and buying in the same market, and their next building site was an expensive purchase, half an acre for £112,500.

Searching for this plot proved extremely difficult, but in April 1989, they found what they were looking for. It was a superb double building plot, in a conservation area, on the edge of one of Kent's picture book villages.

The land had been part of the garden of an old house and had been on the market for some time while various developers tried and failed to get planning permission for a number of houses. The planning committee resolutely refused to allow more than two houses on the one-acre site. The owner of the land was equally resolute in wanting to sell the entire site to one purchaser.

David found a buyer for one half of the site, and bought the whole lot for £225,000 when it went to auction, an event held at Canterbury cricket ground. On the same day that he bought, he was able to sell the other plot. Both owners then put in for detailed planning permission on their respective half acre sites. Both opted for timber frame, with the perhaps unique result that a Potton house now stands side by side with a Medina Gimson house.

The designs are not dissimilar, but the Coxes chose Medina Gimson because they were able to take a standard design (the Commodore) and vary it considerably, so that all their reception rooms, kitchen and three out of the four bedrooms look out over their rear garden to unspoilt farmland. Altering

The Cox family chose a timber frame home from the **Medina Gimson** range for their second self build.

Every detail was carefully thought out, right down to the weather vane on the garage roof.

the internal layout was not the only modification: David and Sue wanted to specify their own staircase, doors and windows. They also wanted the first floor to overhang the ground floor. It is only a very slight overhang, but just enough to give the exterior elevations added interest, and to make a more pronounced feature out of the tilehanging on the first floor.

Detailed planning permission came through in the autumn. This was a winter build and the Coxes moved in during the following May. In the interim, they rented a cottage close by. It enabled David to call in on the site first thing in the morning on his way to work, and last thing at night on his return.

The build was supervised by an architect who charged a fee per visit, most of the sub-contractors whom David and Sue had used on their first house were employed for this one, and David himself did a fair amount of the work, including second fix carpentry and all the decorating.

No real problems were hit, even though this was – in theory at least – a potentially problematic site, on Kentish clay dotted with mature trees largely protected by preservation orders. In the event, just one cherry tree and a silver birch had to be

taken down, while the whole house was moved forward to save a maple. Towering pines in the front garden remain untouched.

Only one major problem was encountered during the entire project, and that was after David and Sue had moved in. It was also a problem so speedily recognised and remedied, that the couple have nothing but praise for Medina Gimson.

The problem was that the floors upstairs were lifting away from the joists, as Sue noticed one morning when vacuuming. This was evidently connected to the slightly greater floor area upstairs due to the overhang, and possibly a sub-contractor's failure to check that the joists were strongly secured. Whatever the cause, it was almost immaterial: Medina Gimson moved all the upstairs floors, and swiftly corrected the problem.

The only other slight hiccup in the build was the large inglenook fireplace in the lounge. The first attempt looked completely wrong, and so the Coxes had it dismantled and a new design built. The huge old oak beam across it was found in a puddle!

The Coxes' new home is an outstanding small country house, into which a lot of thought has been put.

The clever internal use of woodwork and the lovely views add to the feeling of light throughout the house.

There is an impressive cathedral style hall, which goes the full height of the house, and is overlooked by a galleried landing. The hall does take up space, and meant the loss of a fifth bedroom upstairs: but the Coxes have a possible fifth bedroom downstairs anyway, and love the feeling of spaciousness and light. This is an impression added to by their choice of internal glazed doors from Boulton and Paul's extensive range.

On the ground floor, the large fitted kitchen/breakfast room, dining room and splendid sitting room all face over the rear garden, and all have doors on to the terrace outside. The utility room, cloakroom and a study (the room that could become a fifth bedroom) face the front.

Upstairs, three bedrooms take advantage of the stunning views at the rear of the house, with two bathrooms and a guest bedroom at the front.

Joining the house at a right angle is a large double garage with loft space above it. A covered walkway runs between the garage and the utility room.

The house is charming and immaculate, and very much at ease in its setting. Hand made Tudor clay tiles from nearby Ashford, in Kent, were a requirement by the local planning authority, and did add substantially to the cost of the project. However, within 18 months, they were already weathering satisfactorily and attracting favourable comment.

The Coxes' philosophy was to use small local suppliers wherever possible. Their softwood window frames and mahogany window sills came from Icklesham joinery. The fitted kitchen from Orchid Kitchens in Tunbridge Wells was custom made, yet cheaper than anything from a DIY warehouse.

There is really nothing in their new house that they would change, although they feel they might exchange their wall hung radiators for an underfloor central heating system next time.

Sue Cox meanwhile takes immense satisfaction in what they have achieved: *"It really is proof that with self build, you can get exactly what you want. I enjoy talking about it and what it involved, because I feel so strongly that this is the pleasure of self build. I just hope it encourages other people."*

Her husband, of course, needs no such encouragement. It won't, one feels, be long before he is plot hunting for a third time . . .

Cost:

The Medina Gimson frame came to around £13,500.

Plot price: £112,500

Labour and materials, including all fixtures and fittings: £80,000

Total cost of completed house: £210,000

Market value of house on completion: £285,000.

The Coxes seized the opportunity to take one of Medina Gimson's standard designs and adapt it to suit their own tastes.

Case studies: Hands on!

These are two enterprising young families who used self build to leap up the housing ladder. They not only managed the build using sub-contracted labour and buying all their own materials, but they also did a considerable amount of work themselves. The first family's build cost just under £25 per square foot; the second family achieved their build for around £30 per square foot.

Can self build save you money? Ask two Herefordshire families that question, and their answer will be a resounding yes.

The Smalls and the Tylers have both built luxury four-bedroom, two bathroom houses at under £100,000 including the cost of land. Even in today's depressed market, both properties have a current valuation of at least 40 per cent more.

Their achievement is all the more remarkable since neither wife works, both families have small children, and in both cases, budgets were tight.

How did they do it? Both Gary Small and Robert Tyler were able to contribute a fair amount of their own labour and expertise – both work in the building industry; they also went to the same manufacturer for their timber frame, and bought kits that, at around just £13,000 each, were tremendous value for money.

The Tylers

Robert is a bricklayer, but he says that building a brick and block house would never have been his choice: *"Blockwork is never a bricklayer's favourite job. I chose timber frame because I think it's an equally good method of construction, but with none of the mess and a lot more speed. I am convinced timber frame is the thing of the future."*

Robert and Sharon, who have a baby daughter called Jessica, bought their timber frame from Taylor Lane, a ten-year old Hereford company that offers no standard designs of its own, has no glossy sales literature and deliberately doesn't have a brochure.

Instead, it manufactures and supplies each order individually on site, to customers' own designs, using top grade Canadian timber. The company will use architects' designs, and customers can also utilise Taylor Lane's own design services, which will convert any plans into working drawings.

The Tylers were faced with a particularly difficult plot, and went to specialist designer Phil Gill of Hereford *"to see what could be done with it."*

The couple had found the plot, in Hereford itself, after some searching around. The site had outline planning permission for a four-bedroomed house, but the consent seemed optimistic rather than practical.

The plot is around one fifth of an acre, but it is an awkward shape, since it is only 37 feet wide by 200 feet deep. As if the narrowness were not difficult enough, there was also a very large public drain which passed right through the middle of the land. A covenant placed on the land in 1926 which restricted development, was yet another problem that had to be overcome.

Not surprisingly, perhaps, the plot had been on the market for two years. Indeed, most people would have passed by without even realising it was there, since most of its frontage was obscured by an old garage.

The drain, which carried stormwater off the public highway, proved tricky. In order for the site to be developed at all, it had to be taken up and diverted, a task which other would-be purchasers had clearly thought impossible as soon as they realised that the pipe was ten feet down. Diverting the drain was certainly a huge undertaking, but it did allow the Tylers to re-negotiate the price of their plot. They eventually bought it for £34,850, a cut of £5,000. The covenant, which had originally been placed on the land by a now extinct fruit company, cost them £375 in the insurance they were advised to take out against the possibility of anyone trying to enforce the covenant.

The design of their house had to reflect the shape of the site. With a very narrow frontage to contend with, the house itself is narrow and deep, measuring just 26 feet across, by 52 feet long. It has an integral garage at the front, and an unusual internal layout with the sitting room right at the back.
Most visitors find it hard to believe that a house which looks so small at first sight, can be so spacious inside.

In fact, it has four large double bedrooms and two bathrooms upstairs, with lots of space downstairs.

This photograph shows how neatly the Tylers' house fitted into their compact plot.

Note the interesting use of brickwork in the Tylers' fitted kitchen.

Individuality and self expression are key features in a self built home. Here the Tylers chose an arresting bay window.

The airy effect of this unusual stairwell is enhanced by the arch-shaped window and the pale woodwork.

Altogether the house contains 1,900 square feet of very comfortable living space.

Work on the site began in October, 1991. Robert did all the footings and drainage works himself, and the concrete slab was in place in early November. The frame arrived on December 6, and was erected in about nine days with the help of Gary Small. After that, Robert's bricklaying skills came in more than useful, with Sharon acting as hod carrier and providing the labour.

The couple also helped with various other tasks, and Sharon and her father did all the decorating. Sub-contractors were used for all the tasks that Robert felt unqualified to tackle, including plumbing, electrics and drylining. He also used the services of another bricklayer to help clad the frame.

Altogether, the actual build, including kitchen and bathrooms, cost £47,000. Robert and Sharon did use some sub-contractors, but generally they reckon that they did about 50 per cent of the labouring themselves. The whole project, including land, cost £82,000 and their property has a current valuation of £132,000.

Sharon, 27, and Robert, 30, say they did not even find the self build particularly hard work: *"Just really enjoyable,"* says Sharon. *"In fact, we'd like to do it all over again, on a bigger scale."*

Obviously, Robert's bricklaying skills – there were 12,000 bricks and 1,000 blocks in the footings – came in very handy. However, what really enabled this young couple to self build in the first place wasn't their handyman skills, but their ability to see potential in a very difficult plot. *"Initially, our solicitor said don't get it. Later, when he saw what we had done with it, he said it was a very good plot,"* says Robert.

Although Robert had previously worked almost entirely on brick and block houses for a major developer, he knew of Taylor Lane's reputation for competitive prices and good quality timber frames. The result was that he went nowhere else for a quote. He points out that the frame, which cost £12,933 without VAT, included fitted wardrobes and even a fully glazed double patio door. For everything else, the couple shopped around carefully and took quotes from at least three different sources. The biggest cost, they say, lay in finishing the house off, which added another £5,000 to £6,000 to the total bill.

Their bathrooms came from B&Q, and their light oak kitchen from Sharpe and Fishers in Cheltenham.

Major costs, apart from the frame and plot, were employing sub-contractors and buying materials while hire of scaffolding came to £600.

The couple moved in during March 1992, seven months from when the footings were dug. There is, they say, absolutely nothing they would change about their house, and the only thing that still needs finishing off is the patio.

As far as the Tylers are concerned, self build was the only realistic option for them and the only way that this young couple could take a leap up the housing ladder.

The Smalls

Gary and Andrea Small also went to Taylor Lane for their timber frame, and used the same architectural services as the Tylers. They even used the same facing brick, Surrey Appleyard by Arc.

But whereas Robert and Sharon are first-time self builders, Gary and Andrea had already self built once before.

"This time, I found it much easier because of the lull in the building industry. Orders came on time. When we first self built, I remember waiting 18 weeks for the bricks to arrive. Suppliers took the view that you were a one-off customer, and they couldn't be bothered. This time round, they have taken a totally different view," says Gary.

Gary and Andrea, who have two children, Lucy, seven, and Nicholas, five, did not have a narrow plot for the second self build, since it was 75 foot wide and 100 foot deep, but it did have its own problems. They also experienced difficulty selling their previous home in a very slow market, but were sensible enough to decide to complete the sale before embarking on their next venture.

"It took 18 months to sell, purely because it was such a sticky market. We moved because basically, I just wanted to do it all again," says Gary, who is a freelance timber frame erector who works all over the country.

It is not difficult to see why the Smalls fell in love with their plot, which stands in an idyllic position in a very quiet country lane, with glorious farmland views.

The Smalls' plot had a wide enough frontage for them to include an integrated double garage.

It had not been advertised, and they found the plot through an estate agent. It was one of two in the lane. Their next door neighbour is also self building, also for the second time. The site cost the Smalls £40,000 for their share, and they and the neighbour made a joint approach to buy.

The Smalls finally sold their property in June 1991, and moved into rented accommodation for six months. It was obviously important for the build to go ahead quickly – and it did. Work started in July, preparing the site and foundations, the slab was laid in the first week of August, and the timber frame kit arrived on August 13. The target proved perfectly realistic, with the family moving in on December 16, 1991.

The timber frame cost £13,000 plus VAT and, like the Tylers', it included wardrobe doors and glazed patio doors, as well as all the other internal and external joinery.

The foundations did, however, prove costly and took the build over budget. According to original estimates, they should have cost £2,000, but ended up costing £7,000. The hillside site is on clay, and lies on a slope, beneath a steep field. The whole

plot had to be excavated and levelled down to almost the level of the lane in front, because the planners did not want to see too steep an incline up to the house.

But this insistence on levelling the site did raise worries about the amount of rain that could come rushing down off the field on to the plateau which had been created for the plot.

This problem was averted by constructing a deep French drain all round the garden. Water from the field falls into this one-yard deep ditch, which is filled with stones, and it is then diverted round the sides of the plot, away from the house and its septic tank. The French drain was the recommendation of the building inspector; in heavy downpours, it works reassuringly well.

Like Robert, Gary did a fair amount of labouring himself at weekends and evenings and he reckons that he reaped considerable savings. By being able to put the frame up himself, he saved around £2,000. Together with the cost of the land, the entire project came to £100,000, including all finishing touches like the carpets and curtains. Actual build was £58,000. The current valuation

The rear view of the house, showing the French windows and the stone patio.

The brickwork chosen blends well with the guttering and the choice of paintwork.

of this attractive country house stands at anywhere between £140,000 and £160,000.

Gary sees self build from two angles, as not only is he a self builder himself but virtually his entire working life is spent in the same field.

"What inspired me in the first place was working with self builders who had no real practical knowledge. Even so, I could see that they could manage it perfectly well. I thought that if they could, so could I."

A very tight budget dictated careful spending. The kitchen came from Texas Homecare, and Andrea went bargain hunting for soft furnishings in the cheapest places. The result is a family home that feels both luxurious and practical.

Gary and Andrea believe that their house has the perfect layout for family life, with every downstairs room leading off the hall, and every upstairs room leading off the landing.

Accommodation is a generous 1,800 square feet plus garaging and utility. There is a roomy hall, with a large galleried landing, three double bedrooms, and a master suite with its own bathroom and huge walk-in wardrobes – so huge

in fact that it is almost a dressing room.

With its superb setting, this is a family house of the highest standard. Nor is there any problem with what the neighbours think – they self built too!

Costs:

The Tylers

Plot: £34,850

Timber frame: £12,933

Total build cost (including kitchen and bathrooms): £47,000

Total cost of project: (including interest rates): £82,000

Current valuation of house: £132,000

The Smalls

Plot: £40,000

Timber frame: £13,000

Building costs: £58,000

Total inclusive cost of project: £100,000

Current valuation of house: £140,000 (minimum)

The kitchen contains a useful breakfast bar and has a charming outlook over the garden.

Case study: English oak-framed home

This self built home is located in one of Herefordshire's most famous black-and-white villages. It is of particular interest because of the way that this brand new property, by Border Oak, blends so harmoniously into its medieval setting. The houses in this village are built the same way: all that separates them is a few hundred years.

This new property, by Border Oak, was only finished in the summer of 1992, but the first thing to say about it is that it is almost every bit as authentic as the ancient timbered houses which surround it.

Note the 'almost': the major difference seems to be that instead of using wattle and daub – the traditional mixture of woven twigs, straw, mud and manure – a kind of polystyrene has been used as infill between the timbers.

Otherwise, this late 20th century house is faithfully made in the same materials, and to the same building methods that were used in the middle ages.

Chris Anthony, who had this new home built, says: *"Having watched it go up, and seen it built in exactly the way as most houses were constructed so many centuries ago, I cannot tell you how impressed I was. No wonder those old timber frame houses are still standing."*

His new home is not so much a house, it is more a street scene. For it is in fact not one, but two houses, as the planners, seizing the chance to be environmentally sympathetic, wanted to see a terraced row of timbered cottages, complete with pavement.

The building stands on the street edge, a right of way allowing pedestrians to use the sloping pavement that passes by the front door. The front door itself opens straight on to the pavement, under the overhanging first floor. The house stands straight and proud, but completely in harmony with the lovely old houses around which have grown higgledy piggledy over the years.

Small wonder, then, that when planners want to come and cheer themselves up, they come and take a look, says Chris Anthony: *"Once, a party of planners came after a particularly difficult site meeting. One said they just wanted to gaze and reassure themselves they had at least done something right."* In contrast with the planners, the parish council were opposed to the development, although – not surprisingly – local opinion has now softened.

Certainly, the new house looks as if it has always been in this quiet and beautiful village, where there are no supermarkets and no take-aways, just the bustle of small shops, an exquisite church at the bottom of the high street, and a bus service into Hereford every two hours.

Chris Anthony and his wife Frances cared passionately about getting their new home right. They came to Weobley four years ago from Kent, looking for a completely different life. They certainly found it. In Kent, they ran a family hardware shop; in Weobley, they fell in love with and bought a magnificent old pub. The Salutation Arms is at least 600 years old, and possibly even older since it is mentioned in the Domesday Book.

Chris and his wife, a brilliant self-taught chef, have built the pub up to new heights by a mixture of sheer hard work and dedication. As well as running the bars, they do bed and breakfast, and their dining room attracts customers from miles around. But living as well as working in the pub had its disadvantages: *"We love the old inn, but we never got away from the job. We wanted to build something just like the Salutation, with all the character but with none of the problems of upkeep and heating that come with such an old building,"* explains Chris. *"It was also vital to live close by."*

When the couple bought the pub, with it went a tiny patch of land on the opposite side of the narrow road. It had no planning permission, but was sold with 'hope value'.

The land was an open site, on a slope and only 28 feet wide, with nothing on it, although older memories recalled it being part of a larger site which had had a barn, a pig stye and a woodshed up until 1947. Some of this site had already been sold for the development of a modern bungalow – the kind of building more at home in suburbia than in Weobley.

The Anthonys did not even consider a modern looking house, and rejected pressure (and, unbelievably, there was some) to build in brick.

The couple knew from an early stage that their best bet was to go for full detailed planning consent.

This attractive pair of Border Oak cottages blends well with the surrounding village scene. No wonder Chris and Frances Anthony look proud.

Had they sought a vague outline permission first, in the usual way, they felt it would have been rejected out of hand.

The Anthonys approached several companies and told them of their ideas. Two companies expressed particular interest in the project: *"Border Oak impressed us, and another deciding factor was that they were able to offer Foundation 15 as a building guarantee."*

Negotiations followed. There was a three-way conversation between Border Oak, the Anthonys and the local planners, who were so keen to see a street scene rather than a single house that they originally wanted an application for three two-bedroomed terraced houses. In the end, the site proved simply too tiny, and in October 1991, detailed permission was given for a pair of adjoining cottages. The Anthonys planned to live in the larger of the two cottages, aiming to sell or rent out the other.

Right from the start, Border Oak's dedication was impressive – which is not perhaps surprising, given the company's known commitment to English vernacular architecture. John Greene, the director, says that his firm specialises in unpretentious designs, using local materials with an inherent sense of scale and evidence of the 'hand of man'. That is no fancy statement: Border Oak's carpenters have revived the forgotten skills of Elizabethan carpenters who worked on timber house frames, made in solid English oak.

Border Oak's frames are made traditionally, with mortice and tenon joints secured by oak pegs. Each Border Oak house is different, but each is built in a system of oak and truss 'bays' (in medieval times, people spoke of a house with so many bays very much as today one would speak of a house with so many bedrooms).

This bay system not only allows different layouts, but because it is modular, also overcomes the problems of difficult and challenging sites.

Few could have been more challenging than the narrow, sloping, roadside site in Weobley. The Anthonys could have sub-contracted the laying of the foundations; instead, because getting the foundations right was so critical, they deemed it wise to hand over the entire project to Border Oak, from start to finish, for a total contract cost of £110,000.

The foundations had to go down deep, and the diggers uncovered old footings and a stream bed. Because of the slope, the lower floor had to have a block and beam construction, while the upper one had an ordinary slab. The foundations were then faced with stone to give a plinth effect.

Considering the many technical problems, it is almost unbelievable that work proceeded so smoothly at all times from the moment it started on January 6, 1992 until it finished on June 6. The tiny plot meant that no building materials could be stored on site. Instead, the beams for the frame were put in the pub car park opposite, where a crane was stationed, and were then swung across the road. Scaffolding also stood out in the road, but luckily just inside the notional highway. This meant that the road into the village stayed open at all times.

Because the Anthonys could not afford to lose custom at the pub by having their car park out of action, it was essential that the huge oak beams were moved on to the site as quickly as possible. *"When I saw how many there were, and the sheer weight of each one, I didn't see how it could be done. Yet, the frame was erected by a team of three men inside five days, and I had the car park back when I needed it at the weekend,"* said Chris.

The two adjoining cottages are divided by a wall of solid block. This is not structural, but is there for fire safety purposes.

Once all the beams were up, pink polyurethane panels – in fact, Urethane foam building boards – were put in place. In the olden days, builders would have used wattle and daub for the infilling. Wattle is woven twigs, and daub is a mixture of what came to hand in medieval times: manure, mud, horse hair and straw were all commonly used.

John Greene of Border Oak explains: *"We have built with wattle and daub, and can do it, although we tend to leave out the manure. However, polyurethane boards have exceptional insulating properties."*

The panels are pink, and when they were in place, the Anthonys had fun teasing people that this was the colour the house would stay. In fact, the panels were finished in a neutral render, which will be left to weather naturally, as was always the case. *"It wasn't until the Victorians got their hands on these timbered houses that they were painted black and white."*

The beams, too, have been left their natural colour, and as the years go by, will mellow and season according to the weather. This process has already started at the far end of the lower cottage, which receives most sunshine.

Each infill panel is edged with neoprene, a type of foam which forms a seal no matter how much the timber expands or shrinks as it is bound to do. Each panel also has its own damp proof course, all part of a unique system patented by Border Oak.

Externally, the cottages were finished with plastic guttering (cast iron proved just too expensive for the Anthonys) and old Welsh slates on the roof.

Internally, the second fix took a painstaking six weeks, and the Anthonys themselves took particular pleasure in finishing off the woodwork, staining and waxing the beautifully turned staircases, the doors and all the window frames.

They moved in to the larger of the cottages in July 1992, and have since found it beautifully warm, thanks to the insulated floors and walls, the inglenook fireplace and the electricity 7 heating system.

Their praise for Border Oak is unqualified. As the build ended, near-identical snag lists were produced by both the company and the Anthonys, and problems corrected. The only significant one was a soakaway which had to be relaid.

In total, the Anthonys spent about £115,000 on the two cottages, the smaller one of which has been valued at £75,000. Chris Anthony feels that talking about money and savings is almost irrelevant, since

the build was always about getting something absolutely right, not about making economies. He also points out that he already owned the land and so cannot put a plot price into his accounts.

In the beautiful little village of Weobley, the cottages take their place, as naturally as the 600 year old houses around. They are a talking point for visitors, provide stress relief for the planners, and are a source of pride locally which is particularly satisfying considering the initial doubts and opposition.

But the important thing is that the Anthonys have a perfect home: *"It's wonderful, full of appeal and character. Everything we could have dreamed of in a home that is so special."*

The cottages are exactly 15 feet wide internally downstairs, but 18 inches wider upstairs, with the first floor jettied out. The whole plot is 28 feet wide, but some of this is taken up by the pavement at the front. At the back, a small paved area provides a patio garden, ideal for the Anthonys since they are too busy to spend time cultivating a lawn and plants.

Chris and Frances were so keen to have a genuinely authentic home that they decided against double glazing on the grounds that it just wouldn't have looked right.

Border Oak specialises in authentic English architecture, eschewing what it calls gimmicks and false touches. Not all their work features oak frames; some of their traditional buildings are in cob or masonry and some have thatch. The company also offers advice on fitting out – everything from flagstones to dovecotes and even roses round the door!

The oak frames are made and put together in the workshops. Then, carpenters mark each piece of wood to identify it. The frames are then taken down and, following the wood marks, re-assembled on site. The wood marks, traditional in old houses, remain an attractive feature.

The exposed internal beams add to the traditional feel of the house.

The extensive use of exposed wood throughout the cottage contributes to the rustic air. This is the jettied first floor.

Case study: Special needs home

This study focuses on a large single-storey house in Oxfordshire, which was especially built for a woman with multiple sclerosis. Although she did not manage the build on a day to day basis, Mrs Brenda Hutt had considerable say in the design and in all the features that would give her optimum independence. As a direct result of the success of this, she is now a professional in her field, and works as a consultant in special needs housing. An interesting feature of this case study is the difficulty in winning planning permission, and how this challenge was successfully overcome.

Stepping into Brenda Hutt's beautiful timber frame home on the outskirts of a village, there is absolutely nothing about it that immediately shrieks 'disabled'.

In fact, the label – if there has to be one – should really read 'enabled'.

That is because building this striking Scandinavian-style single-storey has enabled Brenda to carry on living exactly where she wants to be.

That is in her home village, one of those strikingly beautiful and quintessentially English places in Oxfordshire, where pub, church, cottages and farms cluster round a cricket green, and where roads become lanes that disappear into country tracks.

But this is a village that is also much more than just a pretty face. For it is here that caring friends, neighbours and helpers abound. Many of those who pop in – to do her shopping or walk her dog – have known Brenda for years, ever since she was a young mum suddenly struck down by multiple sclerosis. At 32, Brenda found herself progressively disabled, and living with her husband and baby son Ben (now a rugby-playing teenager) in a large two-storey house. They had moved there in the first place intending to fill it with children, one for every bedroom.

The MS put paid to that, and as the illness took hold, Brenda found herself becoming almost imprisoned inside the house. Simply moving around inside it, in a wheelchair, was increasingly difficult. Going into the garden was fraught with obstacles, and became impossible unaided. If it had not been for a busy working life, running a company with her then husband, Brenda's horizons would have become sadly restricted.

It became gradually obvious that Brenda needed to live on one level in a bungalow, but over a period of several years, not one that was suitable came up for sale; nor did any plots of land – hardly surprising in a conservation area. Brenda was keen to build a bungalow herself, but not at all keen to have to do so away from her friends, neighbours and her local support systems.

As Brenda says: *"If community care means anything, it must mean that the community in which you live has to be the best place to give you that care. Was it fair that I should have to leave the community where I had lived for 14 years simply because my housing needs could not be met?"*

There was only one possible solution: to build a bungalow in the garden of the Hutts' large house.

Achieving planning permission was an uphill battle.

The planning authority had excellent grounds for rejecting the application, arguing that the plot was backland development; an "unwanted extension" of the village; an infill plot; and whose access was also on a dangerous bend in the road.

Not one of these points could be denied. Brenda was, however, determined to battle, because she felt so strongly that the main arguments were not planning but human issues.

The day before her application was due to be heard, with a strong recommendation for refusal, she went to see her MP Michael Heseltine.

"He instantly grasped the situation, and was very much at ease with me and my wheelchair," Brenda recalls. *"He's a doer, not a waffler, very much a man of the people."*

Michael Heseltine's intervention saved the day, because he rang the planning officer and suggested that this was a case where a site visit might be appropriate. This meant a delay, and Brenda made the most of it. With the planning officer still recommending refusal, and her planning consultant having shrugged his shoulders in consequence, Brenda contacted each member of the planning committee to explain her situation.

When eventually her application went before the committee, each member was briefed. Not only that, but there were no fewer than 35 totally

Every aspect of Brenda Hutt's house has been designed with easy access for the wheelchair in mind.

Large picture windows and a simple design structure enable the house to make the best use of the sunlight.

Avoiding awkward joints was one of the most important considerations when laying the floors.

The kitchen was planned with care so that everything is at the right level and within easy reach.

unsolicited supportive letters from people in the village, and not one against.

The application was passed, hedged with the unusual condition that the bungalow was to be built for occupation by Brenda Hutt, and that if this intention were to change before building commenced, the permission lapsed.

Triumphant, Brenda began to look for her new home. She knew she wanted a bungalow, she knew accessibility was high on the list, and she wanted *"a deal whereby I got what I wanted without having to deal with the day-to-day building."* A timber frame package seemed the answer, and she sent off for 'all the catalogues'.

At this stage, the one thing she knew for certain about timber frame was that its internal sound insulation could be questionable.

Wanting to check this, she asked for details; only two suppliers were able to give her the information she wanted. Of these, one was Hosby Sale, at nearby Abingdon.

"I went to see one of their houses in mid-construction, and was totally and immediately hooked," Brenda happily recalls. A standard design

was out of the question, but Hosby Sale assured her that they would build her what she wanted.

Brenda then approached various architects with mixed results. At least one treated her so patronisingly that she felt unable to use him. Others were keen, but it gradually dawned on her that she knew at least as much about practical design for disabled people as anyone else.

The end design was very much Brenda's, with some advice from Patrick Langlois, a freelance architect who often works with Hosby.

Brenda's stunning new home is a 2,000 square foot house with all its accommodation on one floor. The superb wooden floors are a magnificent feature throughout, making the property feel Scandinavian inside despite its more conventionally English external appearance.

There are four bedrooms, two with ensuite bathrooms, a family bathroom, and a large open plan area where all the living rooms flow into each other. The kitchen is at one end, with a utility room leading off it; the kitchen leads into a dining area and family room; from these, you go into a sunny, south facing living room.

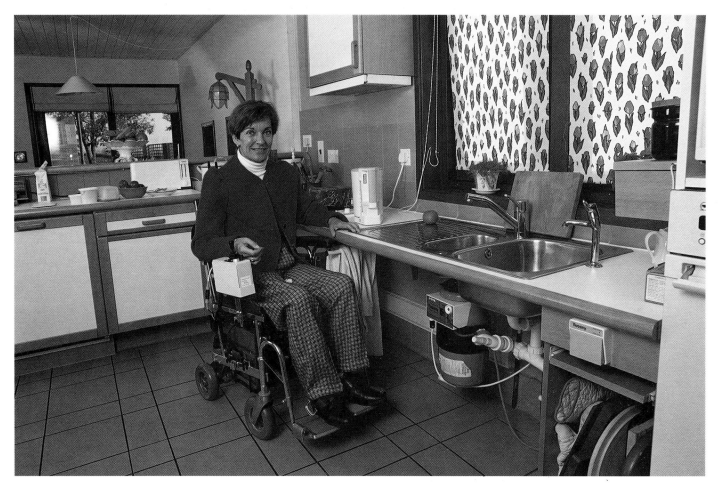

Building the bungalow started in May 1990; Brenda and her son moved in just six months later.

Her new home seems immense – all that space on one level! – to a visitor. To Brenda, the important thing is that it is all usable space even though the touches that enable it to be so, are subtle rather than obvious.

There are no difficult thresholds between rooms, or between house and garden; nowhere for a wheelchair to get stuck.

In the kitchen, the units are fitted low, to be accessed by someone sitting in a wheelchair, and the wheelchair itself can get under the sink. The kitchen was fitted with Invita units made in Denmark. Hosby's joinery team adapted the heights, and Brenda uses pull-out baskets instead of shelving for most storage. Even the Bosch fridge and freezer have drawers rather than shelves.

In her bedroom, the lights are operated not by switches but by highly sensitive touch controls which allow them to be turned on, off or be dimmed, and the curtains are electrically operated.

Brenda's shower room is simply a variation of the wet floor bathrooms which are standard in Scandinavian homes. Large and open plan, so that she can use it easily from her wheelchair, there is no difficult shower cubicle to negotiate. Water can go anywhere, and drains away centrally. The floor is non slip, and the toilet wall-hung with all pipework tidily hidden away.

In the utility room, the washing machine has been raised on a plinth, so that Brenda doesn't have to bend down to put clothes inside.

The hallway is very wide, as are all the doors (although that's a standard Hosby Sale feature). Brenda uses a central vacuum cleaner, with suction points throughout the house so that all she needs for cleaning is an easily portable pipe and brush.

Warmth was a very important factor in the design process, partly because of the open plan design with very large expanses of glass, and partly because Brenda's inability to exercise means she feels the cold.

The house has Hosby's standard heat re-cycling system, a mechanical ventilation with heat recovery. All the windows are insulated to the equivalent of triple glazing, and there is electrical skirting board heating. Window latches are easy to use, and accessibility of light switches and electric sockets

was part of the design. A generator has been installed outside, to provide electricity to key areas in the house in the event of a power cut, frequent enough when living in the country.

For security reasons, an entry phone system was installed; the main door can be opened at the press of a button in different parts of the house.

Outside, a car port is on the same level as the front door, so that Brenda can easily get to and from house to car and vice versa. Perhaps best of all is her garden. In her old house, it was the ultimate frustration not being able to use it; in her new house, she happily uses the large wooden deck that runs round two thirds of her house, giving a large sheltered outdoor area beneath the wide eaves with concealed guttering above – another standard Hosby feature.

Beyond the wooden deck is a slope to the lawned garden, so that is accessible too. The whole property looks out on to unspoiled farmland.

The entire project has been such a success for all concerned, that Brenda now works with Hosby, advising on housing where there is a special need.

"I feel so strongly that disabled people must be enabled to stay in their communities. We are, after all, ordinary people, albeit with special physical needs which need to be met in our homes.

"With my own home, I've been able to take on a whole new lease of life. Since living here, I feel that I am treading new water. I am as independent as possible, my home has been planned for my present and my future needs, and I am amongst my friends and community."

Brenda's house cost **£220,000,** completely finished and fitted. This price excludes the land, which she already owned. At getting on for **£110** a square foot (the car port is an extra 350 square feet), this could not be described as cheap. However, it did literally include everything, from the fitted kitchen to some of the specialist fittings. Certain items added to the price, for instance, the generator at **£4,886.25.** The planners also insisted on a slate roof, which added **£6,000** to the bill.

Case study: Costed to the last nail

This is a textbook self build, the story of a couple who did everything right! They self built a timber frame home in Cumbria from start to finish over one summer. It is of particular interest from the management viewpoint, especially the way detailed records of costs were kept.

For Peter and Jan Nicholls, this was their second chance to self build. The first time, they had built a brick and block semi as part of a joint project with Jan's sister. When Jan's sister sold up – to build a timber frame – Peter and Jan decided to follow suit.

Jan explains: *"When we first built four years ago, it cost us just £35,000 including land. We were very happy there, but it made sense to move. We had had another child and needed more space. We also knew we could make a reasonable profit on the house, and build something really very nice."*

The couple located a plot of land which was then part of a farm, achieved planning permission and did all their planning. Then they sold up and by

sheer luck, found a tiny bungalow to rent right next door to their building site.

Jan explains: *"Choosing timber frame was important to us, simply because of the speed. Having sold our first house, we did not want to live in rented accommodation for a day longer than we had to. In this area it is expensive, and we didn't feel renting was fair on our three young children, who were having to share a room."*

The site they found, on the edge of a village near Seascale, Cumbria, had had planning difficulties, and the local parish council opposed the application. Jan wrote to the planning authority giving reasons why she thought it should be passed. The authority wrote back saying they would arrange a site visit before deciding.

Jan and Peter were not allowed to attend the site visit, but 'a minibus of councillors' turned up. The result was that planning consent was given, on condition that the access was improved, with two passing places put in.

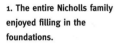

1. The entire Nicholls family enjoyed filling in the foundations.

1.

The couple approached Guardian Homes, timber frame construction specialists, for whom they have nothing but unqualified praise. *"They were absolutely brilliant, with us every step of the way,"* said Jan. The final design was not a standard design, but a blend of everyone's ideas – a four bedroomed, 2,200 square foot house with a separate garage. Guardian Homes provided the plans for both planning and building control, and with approval in place, work started on site in early June.

The couple were able to move in just over four months later with daughters Michelle, 10, Laura, eight, and son Jason, four.

Right from the start, the most important factors in the self build were time and money. Peter and Jan had a tight budget which they controlled very carefully , and it was important that they did not slip a day here or there in the build.

They had £50,000 capital from the sale of their first house, which was enough to buy the land and the timber frame, and pay for furniture storage and professional fees. The rest of the money was advanced in stages from the North of England Building Society, whose service was excellent.

"They would come and inspect the build and within the next week, the cheque would be available for the next stage," enthused Jan. *"This was no mean feat, because with the sheer speed of progress, some of the stage payments were being made very close together. Yet there was never a delay, never a time when we had to hang around for the money."*

Costings had been put together for them by Guardian Homes, and the couple's target was to stick to these. Everyone realised the need for a healthy contingency.

"The great unknown is always going to be the foundations, because you really don't quite know what to expect until you get in there," said Jan. *"You really must have a leeway. If you don't spend it, you've still got it at the end of the build, and then you can spend more on the bathrooms and kitchen. In our case, we did need the leeway because we had to raise our finished floor level to accommodate the drainage requirements, and the foundations cost twice what we had hoped. However, after this, we made sure of making savings in other areas, and so we finished the build with money in hand to spend on good quality fittings."*

2. The house begins to take shape as the timber shell is erected.

2.

The package, including supply and erect, cost £25,715 for the house and the garage. The build was checked by an architect, who issued progress certificates and seemed incredibly good value at a fee of just £225. The couple set themselves different tasks in the self build: Jan's was to financially manage the whole thing, while Peter – who continued his job as a process worker throughout – managed the site, often working alongside his sub-contractors.

"All the way along, he did lots of work, contributing his labour whenever he could. The result was a very happy, enjoyable build, with excellent relationships with all our sub-contractors. They were all fabulous. I feel this is a very important point: if you treat people well, you'll get good work out of them," advised Jan.

The speed of the build was also helped by the fact that every sub-contractor was available when needed. The couple point out that they used only local people; the only delays they experienced were when large, well known companies were unable to supply on time.

Jan kept meticulous records throughout, noting every single invoice separately as it came in, so that the couple would be able to re-claim their VAT as soon as possible. This proved the case, and the £3,000 the couple got back then promptly paid for carpets and soft furnishings.

Having had experience of building both brick and block and timber frame, Peter and Jan say that their decision to build timber frame the second time has paid off: *"The speed of construction was a major saving. With our first house, we had to wait weeks before it had dried out enough for us to move in, and even then, we probably moved in too soon.*

"This time we moved in the moment it was finished. Of course, there were still things to do, but every piece of wood had received two coats of stain, the whole house was decorated and more importantly, it was safe for the children."

The house is also proving warm and energy efficient: *"We have electric storage heaters, the same system as we had at our previous house. Although this is a larger property, we have exactly the same number of heaters, turned down lower. We are looking forward to comparing our bills over a long period."*

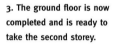

3. The ground floor is now completed and is ready to take the second storey.

3.

Peter and Jan emphasise how much they enjoyed the build and how pleased they are with the end result. They have no plans to self build again, this being the house of their dreams. They took 'hundreds' of snapshots throughout, and also made a video.

In particular, they enjoyed looking round for bargains, like the 600 year old ship timber which cost just £25, and is now a feature in the kitchen. They also make the point that being polite and friendly reaps dividends. All sub-contractors were treated to tea and home-made goodies; all callers on site were made welcome; and the building inspector was always treated with respect. In return, Peter and Jan enjoyed successful relationships with everyone, as evidenced by the huge bouquet of flowers Jan received from Guardian Homes on moving in day.

Costs

Plot: £22,000

Build costs:

Kit (house, garage, including erection) £25,714
Site insurance: £338.00
Architect: £225.00

Plans: £352.50

First Building Regulations: £66.00

Second Building Regulations: £175.00

Water (connection): £635.00

Telephone installation: £119.44

Builder (foundations/drains/brickwork): £4,400.00

Bricks: £2,002.63

Blocks: £397.96

Sand: £198.00

Other foundation costs: £80.00

Digger hire: £420.00

Pipes (stack and water): £930.00

Concrete: £1,490.44

Hardcore: £851.76

Septic tank: £599.25

Scaffold hire: £500.00

Sandstone sills: £350.00

Lintels: £79.82

Whacker plate hire: £24.77

House/garage roof, labour and materials: £1,866.00

4. The erection of the upper storey in progress, with the roof trusses standing ready for their turn.

5. The finished timber shell is now ready to take the roof tiling.

Joiner (labour): £1,200.00

Joining materials (misc): £210.00

Bathroom: £1,710.00

Kitchen and appliances: £3,300.00

Decorating (paint, tiles, curtains, etc) £1,500.00

Fireplace: £600.00

Utility units: £103.50

Internal doors: £467.74

Vents: £93.12

Bifold doors: £182.00

Total, including plot, : £79,939.02

Reclaimed VAT was about £3,000

The insurance company made the Nicholls insure the house for £125,000, which they say is its rebuild value, excluding the land. Note that the figures do not include legal fees of nearly £1,000 (for the sale of the previous house as well as for the land purchase), or furniture storage which came to £340.

Electrician: £670.00

Electrical materials: £793.00

Electric heating system & water heating: £1,267.09

Electricity connect-up: £225.00

Plumbing labour: £600.00

Plumbing materials: £497.00

Fix plasterboard and skim, and lay screed floor: £2,300.00

Materials for above: £400.00

6. The completed house basks in the evening sunlight.

Case study: Never too late to self build

In contrast with an earlier case study which involved a couple of young newlyweds, this focuses on a retired couple whose 900 square foot Wiltshire bungalow is both small and sweet. It may be little, but it has big ideas about cost savings, and the couple who had it built saw their main role as financial management. It was completely finished in less than four months for just under £63,000, including plot. Of particular interest in this case study is the diary that was kept, showing the schedule of events.

A home on a shoestring was what was needed by Nelson and Barbara Woolford, and happily, it's just what they have.

Nelson and Barbara are pensioners whose entire income is the basic state pension. Nelson had to retire early at 61 due to poor health, and the couple have never had an income of more than £100 a week.

They turned to self build simply because it was the only way they could afford a home in the village where they had lived for so long.

And perhaps what their story proves is that you don't have to be rich to be a self builder and nor do you have to build a gin palace.

Work on the foundations started on January 6 1992, and the couple were able to move into their new home, which was by then completely carpeted, curtained and decorated, on April 1.

Nelson, now 67, and his wife Barbara had lived in the same 1930s semi for 32 years. However, Nelson suffers from chronic bronchitis, and was finding it difficult to cope with the increasing maintenance, and the costs involved, of a house of that age.

For some years, they had wanted to move into a bungalow where they could enjoy their retirement without having to worry about either stairs, or expensive upkeep.

Unfortunately, their village, near Swindon, Wiltshire, had become increasingly popular and expensive to live in over the years.

Property prices meant that they could not even afford a retirement flat, let alone a bungalow; but they did not want to move away from the area, and away from their social life (both are keen bowlers), friends and relatives.

It was a classic problem, only resolved when they began to investigate the idea of self build.

Here, they were helped by their son Martin Woolford, director of Home Build Services, a company of consultants specialising in private home build. He was keen to see his parents settled.

Astonishingly, a small piece of land became available, not just in the same village but in the very same road.

But could Nelson and Barbara, on their very limited incomes, afford to go ahead with the purchase? Martin's company drew up careful costings, which included every possible cost element and specification, and presented these to the local National Westminster bank. To everyone's relief, they agreed to fund the project.

An offer, of just under £28,000, was submitted for the long and narrow plot, measuring 150 by 36 feet, and planning permission sought.

The couple needed some reassurance that all would go well, as son Martin explains: *"Barbara is a worrier, and she was very concerned that the build cost should not be greater than had been budgeted, and so she kept a close eye upon the money situation, throughout the whole project."*

Barbara adds: *"We were advised not to exceed our budget at all, as every little extra mounts into a sizeable sum without you realising it. Our total budget was so small that we simply could not afford to spend more money than we had.*

"I made it my job to make sure that if we had to spend more in one area, we cut back in another."

One particular worry was that although the couple's existing home was on the market, it had not been sold by the time contracts were exchanged on the land. The purchase of this was completed on October 23, 1991, and full detailed planning consent given in early December.

Just before Christmas, the site was cleared, ready for work to begin. Nelson, who had worked in the administrative department of a major electrical group before he retired (although in earlier days he was in the building industry) became the site foreman. He spent most of the hours of daylight on the site, helping where possible, and always keeping an eye on progress.

"I lost a stone in weight, and have been told by the hospital that I'm better now than I have been for years," he says. *"Done properly, building a home can be good for your health."*

The couple used the management services of HBS, who are agents for Guildway Timber Frame.

After building started, the Woolfords were relieved a fortnight later to receive an acceptable offer on their own house, with completion of purchase set for early March.

This, however, meant that the bungalow had to be completed quickly, and a target of 12 weeks was set, not just to finish building, but to make the bungalow ready for occupation.

Meanwhile, the couple busied themselves looking for bargains in the January sales. They found a former showroom set being sold off cheaply, and snapped up a complete set of kitchen units and tiles for just £420.

The timber frame was delivered on February 3 and erected at lightning speed. Roof trusses were put on the following day, and the whole property was weatherproof within four days.

Nelson kept a diary of events from start to finish and the twelve weeks flew by in activity. On March 5, the couple duly completed on the sale of their house and moved out, to stay with friends and members of their family. In their new home, the builders were busy working on second fix, and they moved out after finishing everything, on March 20.

Decorating, laying carpets, and hanging the curtains followed, and the couple moved in on April 1. The only snag was that they were without running water for four weeks, due to the water authority's failure to do the connection work until April 28.

Barbara says: *"This was the only hassle we had. We had paid in February for the connection, but despite repeated requests, the work simply wasn't done. Unfortunately, you can't go anywhere else for water."*

This, however, turned out to be the sole problem. Nelson says: *"So many people could not believe the speed with which the bungalow was built that we have had a constant stream of visitors who all seem keen to find out if they can do it."*

Nelson and Barbara Woolford realised their dream when they built this compact bungalow in the village where they had lived for over thirty years.

This charming bay window makes an interesting feature on the front of the house.

All the necessary appliances have been neatly fitted into the Woolfords' kitchen.

Bryan Powell, director of HBS, however, is convinced that the project could have been done in five weeks rather than twelve. He says that the real key lies in advance planning.

He advises self builders: *"Cost out the build, cash flows, specifications and build programmes before you even exchange on the land. Building societies and banks are much more likely to help if they can see that the customer is well prepared and advised in advance."*

The bungalow, which is affectionately known as the Tardis, was designed by local architect Charles Manning. The timber frame element was crucial to the speed of building, because it meant no delay waiting for 'wet' trades to dry out.

The bungalow's total cost of £62,609 is fully inclusive, counting in planning costs and interest on the bank loan. It ended up nicely under budget, and continues to bear out claims that self build can mean one-third saving on the final market price of the property. Nelson and Barbara's cosy new home had an immediate market valuation of £90,000.

Are Barbara and Nelson happy with the result? One hardly has to ask. *"We've not a penny left in the world,"* Barbara says, *"having used up what little savings we had. But we now have the home we want, where we want it, and with no maintenance worries. To us, it's a miracle."*

Barbara and Nelson admit they took a chance buying the plot before selling their previous house. However, they emphasise that they were very realistic about pricing, and accepted an offer only just above the lowest possible limit they had set themselves.

Diary of the build

October 23, 1991: Exchange contracts on land

December 6, 1991: Detailed planning consent given

January 6, 1992: Building work starts

January 24, 1992: Own house receives acceptable offer

February 3, 1992: Timber frame delivered

February 4, 1992: Roof trusses on

February 7, 1992: Bricks delivered, roof felted and battened.

February 12/13, 1992: Roof tiles delivered and laid, brickwork started.

February 17, 1992: Insulation and plasterboard started

March 2, 1992: Brickwork finished

March 5, 1992: Moved out of house

March 12, 1992: Second fix started

March 20: Builders finish

March 27: Decoration finished, carpets down

April 1, 1992: Barbara and Nelson move in

April 28, 1992: Water finally connected

Costs (original budget: £63,900)

Plot: £27,700

Architect: £500

Planning fees: £400

Foundations, including septic tank drainage: £6,185

Roof, including Redland Renown tiles, leadwork and rainwater goods: £1,875

Brickwork (London Brick sand faced): £3,027

Internal fixing plasterboard, insulation, drylining: £1,330

Electrics, including night storage heating points: £1,380

Night store heaters: £3,600

Plumbing, including bathroom suite: £1,280

Second fix carpentry: £450

Kitchen units and tiles: £420

Decoration: £300

Services: £2,880

Fencing/garden/patio: £150

Garden shed: £140

Carpets, curtains, fittings: £950

Interest (Nat West, from December 1 to March 6): £1,200

Legal fees on purchase of land: £342

Total: £62,609.

Case study: Steel framed house in London

This study is by no means a traditional build. It features a house with a steel, rather than a timber frame, and is included here precisely because it is unusual. That said, the principles of construction are the same, and the benefits of erection identical.

What does an architect self build for his own occupation? Answer: a steel framed house. This was the choice of Alan Camp, and the highly successful outcome is a striking multi-purpose building. Visitors remark that they do not know whether it is a house, a warehouse, a workshop or a gallery. What they do know is that when they cast their eyes upwards, they see a rooftop conservatory three floors up.

Alan and his wife Sokari Douglas Camp, with their two small children, find this the ideal living and working environment. Their home provides both workspace and a gallery for Sokari's remarkable and very large metal sculptures.

The house is as remarkable inside as out. Dominated by a large atrium with a spiral staircase which links the three floors, this cathedral-like space has a practical purpose – it houses Sokari's metal palm trees. Outside, the building has shock value in a drab South London street, which was once notorious as the heart of London's gangland.

The area is still rather rough, but it is on the up. And that, as much as anything, is due to the Camps' extraordinary house, that was actually designed and built to look like a converted warehouse. That it does so is no accident, since a warehouse was originally what the couple wanted to buy and convert.

The couple were keen to start a family, but Sokari wanted to work from home. Since her sculptures are on a very large scale, it was clear that only a warehouse – or something like it – would have the right proportions.

When the couple began looking, however, the property market was riding high and warehouses were expensive. Eventually, they found one in the Elephant and Castle area of London. It was too small, but close by was a site which interested them, although its potential was far from obvious at first.

When the Camps first saw it, it was a complete mess – a piece of derelict land, only one tenth of an acre in size, and totally unpromising.

It had once had five houses on it, which were demolished in 1939. Since then, it had been used to store old vehicles and tyres. Owned by Southwark council, it had been designated 'light industrial' in what is a very mixed area of houses, flats, patches of wasteland, temporary Portakabins where various community activities take place, and warehouses.

"It was a really nasty site," Alan recalls. *"the council didn't know what to do with it. None of the neighbours wanted it to be light industrial, but we were told there was no chance of a change of use."*

He was, however, completely undeterred: *"As soon as I saw it, I went straight round to the council."*

He then put in a planning application based on mixed use classification, half domestic and half industrial. Both elements were perfectly genuine.

The couple were looking for somewhere both to work and live; not just a home, but somewhere for Sokari to weld and hammer her sculptures.

Alan's warehouse design for the huge 5,000 square foot building could have proved controversial. Yet at the planning meeting, people from the neighbourhood turned up to beg the committee to approve it.

Their support astonished Alan – *"People never turn up at planning meetings to support applications, only to oppose them"* – and was the start of a thriving relationship with the local community.

The application went through, and work started, with Alan managing the build. Incredibly, from start to finish, the whole house took just 12 weeks. Speed was considered a priority because in a tough part of London, Alan felt uneasy about leaving the site untended for long.

First the plot had to be cleared of layers of old rubbish. There were immense problems at foundation stage because the topsoil had been disturbed so much in the past that attempts to dig straight trenches simply crumbled.

Eventually, however, after a lot of extra concrete and expense, the foundations were completed and the slab laid.

These 'before' and 'after'
photographs demonstrate
how effectively the open
space at the top of the
house has been converted
into a conservatory.

Once the steel frame has been set up and the timber wall panels positioned, the next stage is installing the insulation.

The method of construction, a steel frame, with timber infill panels, was the key to its speed. The frame itself was up within a week, erected by three men and a crane. At that stage, the building looked exactly like an industrial warehouse.

Next the infill panels, made of good quality Canadian Douglas Fir, were put in place. These replaced the blockwork which Alan had originally intended to use within the steel framework - an idea he subsequently rejected because as an architect, he is a believer in timber frames.

"I had designed a very large timber frame at Michael Caine's country home," he explains. *"I was keen on the whole idea for myself, and by using timber rather than blocks, construction was speeded up and costs were reduced by about 20 per cent."*

A further consideration was the very good insulation that could be incorporated with timber panels: *"This is a large house, but our gas and electricity bills are very reasonable,"* says Alan.

One of the biggest jobs of the whole build was putting up the plasterboard inside. The internal walls were then skimmed. Externally, brickwork

clad the steel frame, and a roof of artificial slate tiles with Velux windows was put on. Internally, the second fix proceeded at the same time: plumbing, electrics, joinery and then decorating.

With a fitted kitchen in place, the couple and their baby daughter Ininaa moved in, to a house which has drawn nothing but praise and admiration for its strikingly innovative design.

The huge ground floor is open plan, with the kitchen occupying two adjoining wall areas at one end and the sitting room area focused round an open fireplace. A vast dining and hall area is also used as gallery space for Sokari's sculptures.

The steel palm trees, nearly as tall as the 30 foot high house itself, tower up into the atrium, past the second floor and into the third. Off the ground floor, to one side, is Sokari's workshop, self-contained, with a shower room and storage space.

Up the spiral staircase to the second floor, there is a distinct change of mood. Flexible accommodation includes four bedrooms, each with an ensuite bathroom. The very large landing area is play space for the two children, and a study area for Alan. In the future, this space can quickly be re-modelled to provide more bedrooms.

Up the spiral staircase again to the top floor, where a large conservatory full of plants, peace and light, opens out on to two terraced garden areas with panoramic views over London. Here, there is a children's sandpit, a paddling pool, and room for adults to sit of an evening and drink in the distant glimpses of St Paul's Cathedral.

These rooftop gardens are important, as the house takes up virtually all its site at ground level, with only a forecourt at the front for car parking. At the back, a two foot space between the house and a listed wall behind has been covered in, and is now used for storage.

The house works extremely well, both as home and workspace. There is little the Camps would change about it, even though the somewhat dizzying spiral staircase winding round the atrium makes some visitors nervous. However, the smallest child has no difficulty with it.

Despite its stunning originality, the house mostly features standard items, such as the windows, central heating radiators, bathrooms – no bath cost more than £70 – and light fittings – none of which came to more than £8. The sheer size of the house meant that Alan could negotiate bargains on the basis that he was bulk buying. That way, he saved money on bathrooms, blinds (the house has no curtains) and materials. Even the staircase is not a designer item, but the type that goes outside fire stations. It is made from pre-stressed steel rods clad with reconstituted stone.

The downstairs flooring looks fabulously expensive, wood covering almost one-tenth of an acre. It is in fact cost-effective stained Russian whitewood, with five layers of yachting varnish. The fireplace was made from a kit.

Easily the most expensive feature is the marble flooring in the entrance hall area, made from especially imported Italian marble and laid by an Italian artisan to a design by Alan.

The overall impression of this remarkable building is not just that it is light, airy and obviously artistic, but that it is also a completely practical family home.

The house has been an enormous success in its community, too. Adjoining sites in the street subsequently got planning permission for the same kind of innovative design and mixed use as the Camps' house. What started off as a self build project has effectively transformed a community.

Alan's advice to self builders: *"Be bold! You don't have to build a conventional mock Tudor or Elizabethan house. Don't be afraid to use your imagination and do something different. I believe that what I have here is a real house for the nineties. It is not elaborate, nor over-expensive, nor greedy on materials. It went up quickly, and offers simplicity – almost austerity – of design.*

"I also believe that in the nineties, people should look to this type of building, where they can both live and work. Homes, I hope, will become more multi-purpose."

Cost:

The house worked out at about £37 per square foot to build.

The plot cost £50,000, **and building** £150,000. **On completion, the house was immediately valued at** £450,000.

The frame was from Prestoplan.

The stunning originality of the Camps' self built house makes it stand out in a London street.

Case study: A DIY approach

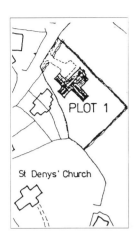

The Robertsons had had their eye on this half-acre plot high up in a remote Welsh village for some time.

This is one of the most unusual projects since the self builder, a carpenter, designed and made his own frame. He, his wife and friends also largely built their home, and gained enormous satisfaction from this hands-on involvement. Their home was designed by an architect, who needed not only to follow his clients' brief but also to observe the very tight criterion laid down for its development.

Tony Robertson and his wife, Jennie, and their three daughters had been living in Teddington for twelve years. However, all of Jennie's immediate family had moved to Wales and settled happily in Cardiff. Tired of the noise and overcrowding of the south-east, the idea began to take root that they would follow.

"It had been Tony's lifelong dream to build his own house, and we had read every single issue of Build It *since it came out,"* said Jennie. *"Once it became clear that we would move, it just seemed the ideal opportunity."*

In 1991, one month before they were due to go to Wales, the couple went to the National Self Build Homes Show and met one of the exhibitors, architect Iain Whittaker of Four Square Design. Tony told him of his dream to build his own timber frame: *"Of all the experts we talked to, he was the only one who didn't laugh or say it couldn't be done. Instead he was incredibly enthusiastic and really listened to us about our ideas."*

Everything followed from there. The Robertsons already had a buyer for their house and they had their eye on a plot of land, high up in the village of Lisvane, a few miles out of Cardiff. A couple of miles away, they found a house to rent where they were to stay for a whole year.

The plot was giving them some nervous moments. They had viewed it, fallen in love with it, but on learning its price, had tried to forget about it. They then believed that it had been sold for £130,000.

Later, they learned the sale had fallen through, and they snapped it up for £110,000.

"It still seemed quite a lot, but it is a half acre plot backing on to common land, in a lovely village, and with magnificent views all round," explained Tony.

The land had originally belonged to the Land Authority of Wales, who sold it - because it was in a sensitive area - with a development brief. *"This specified that we had to build a single storey farmhouse style of property, and stipulated the materials we could and couldn't use. For instance, we weren't allowed to have a concrete tiled roof. At first, it seemed terribly restrictive, but actually it did us a favour. I mean, we don't like concrete tiles either."*

Iain Whittaker visited the site, and saw that it has a significant slope. He made the most of this by designing a large single storey house with several different levels, to be built on stepped foundations. Iain also suggested that the Robertsons knock on neighbours' doors, introduce themselves and show them the plans. Always a good strategy, this proved extremely helpful. Neighbours, who had opposed the development in principle, liked both the Robertsons and the design and changed their minds.

Iain Whittaker's practice, Four Square Design, has an enthusiasm for self build but it was more used to brick and block construction than timber frame. Even so, this wasn't a problem. The practice produced not only the drawings for the planning application, but also what was needed for Building Regulations approval. The calculations for the timber frame were done by engineers, Alan Barnes Associates of Reading.

The Robertsons and Nicole and Lesley, their two younger daughters, moved into their rented accommodation on October 26, 1991. On March 13, 1992, they finally bought their land and one week later, started work on the foundations, using a JCB and its driver, and a hired dumper truck.

All the excavated topsoil and subsoil was kept on site, for landscaping later, and a lock-up container was hired to store timber and tools.

The foundations were standard strips, later topped by a suspended wooden floor – plywood on top of wooden joists. *"I never considered a screed,"* said Tony. *"But then I am a carpenter!"*

He had to hunt round for the timber to make his frame, eventually buying imported Canadian spruce from Hill Leigh in Bath. He began making his frame, on site, on May 14, 1992.

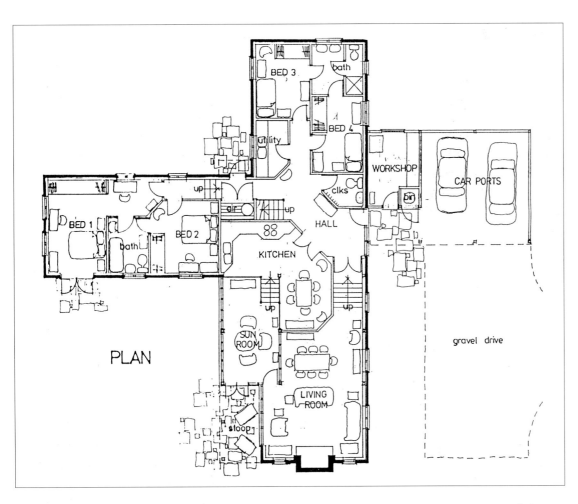

PLAN

The plot was sold with the specific brief that the house built there had to be a single storey farmhouse-type property.

It began going up almost immediately, he and his wife doing all the erection themselves with help from friends in their local church group.

Tony made and erected the frame in sections over a period of six weeks. Unlike a standard kit, pre-fabricated off site and erected within a few days, Tony erected his frame in sections as he made it. The whole process took six weeks. On June 14, the roof trusses started going up – the heaviest of them was lifted into place with a crane that was hired for a day – and again this was achieved in stages over a few weeks.

Tony assembled the sub-frames and made them all on site. The result is an impressively sturdy frame, innovated by Iain Whittaker who has a particular interest in energy efficiency, and different from those commonly available.

Best described as a double frame, it has an outer four inch stud, filled with four inches of insulation, and held in place with the vapour barrier. Then there is a two inch stud which acts as the services duct, and which is also filled with two inches of fibreglass insulation. On top of this comes the plasterboard, which was 12.5 mm thick.

This total of six inches of insulation is in all the walls, the loft, and beneath the suspended floor. Studs are closer than standard.

Tony and Jennie's role in their self build can best be described as maximum involvement. They both contributed their own labour, bought all their own materials, and employed sub-contractors. Sometimes Tony felt he could do all the work himself:

"But it didn't make financial sense. Sometimes it is better to hire somebody else to do the job. We needed to complete the build quickly, and I needed to get back to doing work for other people, to bring in an income."

The actual roofing was sub-contracted, felted and battened, and finished with secondhand Welsh slate that had come off an old school. Brickwork, electrical work by C.J.S. Electric, and all the plumbing by R.M.B. Heating were also sub-contracted, while Tony handled all the joinery, insulation and drylining. He also installed the splendid pine kitchen (found at the 1992 National Self Build Homes Show), the Capapied central vacuum system, and the HRV heat recovery system.

1. Standard strip foundations were used and are seen here being filled in with concrete.

2. Tony Robertson, a carpenter by profession, erected his timber frame in sections over a period of just a few weeks.

3. The suspended timber floor is formed by plywood on top of timber joists.

4. The Robertsons' homemade timber frame is impressively strong and sturdy and includes a total of six inches of insulation.

5. After the roof had been felted and battened, it was tiled with secondhand Welsh slate from an old local school.

The family moved in during October 1992, eight months after starting the build. Although a fair amount of work still needed to be done – landscaping, decorating and flooring – they found their new home highly liveable.

They have also found it extremely warm, with a traditional gas central heating system, powered by a Worcester boiler feeding small but efficient wall-hung radiators. Good mains pressure has enabled them to have a sealed system and saved them having to have a water tank; showers are mains-fed and, despite initial doubts, work very well indeed.

In the lounge area, a Dovre fireplace burns wood and is the last word in good looks and efficiency. In the conservatory area just below the kitchen, a wood burning stove is the focal point.

A delightful house with rooms and living spaces that flow into each other, it offers about 2,400 square feet of flexible, largely open plan living space.

The hall, kitchen and a dining area are all on one level. A staircase leads down to a lower level where there is the conservatory with a further dining area, leading round into the lounge.

Off the hall, each daughter has her own bedroom, with a shared bathroom between each room. There is a similar arrangement with the guest bedroom and the master bedroom also sharing an ensuite bathroom.

Above, is a third level, where there is a huge games room, with a third bathroom. Back down to the hall again, a utility room and a cloakroom complete the picture, while outside is an adjoining double garage area.

Making his own frame and building his own house has been the realisation of a dream for Tony: *"It was what I always wanted to do. I knew I would love doing it, but the reality was even better than the dream,"* he says.

One of the happiest elements of this unusual self build story was the amount of help they had from other people. Neighbours Terry and Joan Davis could not have been friendlier or more helpful. They kept an eye on the site, often popped round with tea and food, and lent a hand too.

Friends did the setting out, and youngsters from their church – the couple became Christians about six years ago – also helped out. *"Please give Phil Gaston, Nathan Smith and his family, and Adam Davies a mention,"* said Tony.

The whole build has come in at a competitive price. Tony believes he saved anything up to £20,000 by making and erecting his own frame. There were further savings by the sheer amount of labour he and Jennie were able to put in.

The overall build, including land, had a budget of around £200,000. The property's current valuation is around £300,000.

But perhaps best of all is the quality of life the Robertson family now enjoy, surrounded by fresh air and wonderful views. As for Tony Robertson, now that he has done it once, he hopes to do it again – for other people. *"Making a timber frame like this is the most satisfying thing I have ever done,"* he says.

But how much did it all cost?

Here are the main sums:

Timber: £31,000

Bricks, cement and sand: £10,000

Fires: £1,500

Kitchen: £7,250

Electrics: £4,000

Plumbing: £4,200

Roof: £5,600

Services: £1,634

Sanitary ware: £3,000

Hire of equipment: £914

Central vacuum system: £528

Heat recovery system: £1,197

Sun room roof glass: £1,077

Guttering: £279

Builders Merchants: £9,885

Sub-contractors: £5,718

Professional fees: £7,162

Total build costs: £94,944. Together with land, the property cost just over £205,000 to build. It has a current market value of around £300,000.

Case study: A professional choice

What do the professionals build for themselves? In 1991, by sheer coincidence, two colleagues in a major construction firm, both self built. Ian Philip and Alasdair Craigie are both civil engineers. They chose timber frame kits, each taking a standard design and modifying it to his own requirements.

Ian Philip and Alasdair Craigie, joint managing directors of a large Scottish construction company based in Aberdeen, both chose Scandia-Hus homes.

Ian and Alasdair, of Chap Construction, are civil engineers who have years of experience in the building industry, from industrial to residential developments to one-off houses. Although they will build anything, including brick and block houses, they believe that Scandinavian timber frame houses are the perfect answer for the extreme weather conditions that can be found in Scotland.

As a result, they have spent more than ten years professionally recommending and building Scandia-Hus homes for no fewer than 90 of their customers. *"The timber frame is of top quality. It is a six*

inch frame, and the supports for the roof trusses are made to withstand a ten foot fall of snow," said Alasdair.

When it came to building for themselves, they did not have to think too hard about what they wanted to build.

"We didn't do it for publicity purposes," Alasdair Craigie insisted. *"It's simply that we genuinely believe in the quality of the product."*

Designed to withstand ferocious winters, Scandinavian houses are popular in Scotland where there is, in any case, a strong tradition of timber frame. *"The television programme that was so damaging to timber frame construction in England was shown in Scotland too,"* said Alasdair. *"But Scots are sensible people. Timber frame has continued to account for at least half of all new houses in Scotland."*

If both men were originally impressed by the solidity and manufacturing quality of these imported Swedish homes, they also liked the flexibility of design and many of the details.

The Philips' bungalow is a standard design, the Forsvik, from the Scandia-Hus range, which they have adapted to their own tastes.

The conservatory has a strong
Scandinavian feel, enhanced
by the expanses of light
timber in the ceiling.

The Craigies' roomy six bedroomed house has a guest suite, games room and conservatory and includes lots of space for their three children.

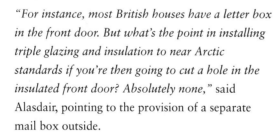

"For instance, most British houses have a letter box in the front door. But what's the point in installing triple glazing and insulation to near Arctic standards if you're then going to cut a hole in the insulated front door? Absolutely none," said Alasdair, pointing to the provision of a separate mail box outside.

Actually living in their new homes has enhanced their appreciation of the product: *"It's answered whatever doubts I might have had,"* said Alasdair. *"For instance, I was never totally sure that the electrical heating system promoted by Scandia-Hus really made economic sense. But having analysed my annual heating bills, which are substantially less than I had expected, I am totally converted."*

His heating system consists of a mixture of electric storage and radiant heaters, to combine both slow response and quick response heating. By designing a Total Control system with at least 60 per cent storage heaters, the Craigie household is able to take advantage of the scheme's special half-rate tariff.

Although Ian and Alasdair built at the same time, using packages from the same supplier, their

houses reflect the different needs demanded by the two families.

Ian's children have left home, so he and his wife Barbara felt they no longer needed their large family house. They have built a smaller bungalow in its grounds. This is a 2,000 square foot Forsvik, a standard design adapted to their own tastes, with a large games room in the attic, a split level sitting room, and a conservatory overlooking the garden.

Ian and Edna Craigie's new house is on a different scale. With three children, Hugh 17, Anne, 15, and Ian 11, they needed space and lots of it. Their new house is a six bedroomed Rowan, which includes a guest suite, games room and conservatory.

Both men were in the fortunate position, unlike most other self builders, of being able to use their own workforce to construct their houses.

Listings

This section has been compiled to be as helpful as possible to self builders of timber frame. Every effort has been made to check that details were correct at going to press, but some may have changed. Most of the suppliers listed below quote six weeks between order and delivery, but anywhere between two weeks and three months seems normal.

The listing includes suppliers of wall panel systems; post and truss frames; and solid timber houses.

Finally, although I have tried to include only reputable companies and their products, readers should obviously make their own inquiries and proceed on that basis. Please note this is not a complete listing of all those active in timber frame and self build.

Anebyhus (UK) Ltd

This company specialises in energy efficient houses with high insulation values, imported from Norway. It offers extensive design flexibility.

Services available: from supplying basic kits to fully-furnished homes. It has a network of regional agents to give local service and advice.

Address: 4 Bell House, Bell Walk, High Street, Uckfield, East Sussex TN22 5DQ, 0825 760169.

Avonside Homes Ltd.

Scottish manufacturer.

Address: Castlecary, Cumbernauld, Glasgow, G68 0DT, 0324 840909.

BergHus Europe Ltd

Makes Swedish homes, but in Britain, using its Architek system. Very speedy erection possible, due to use of large 10-metres long, fully insulated wall panel sections complete with windows and doors.

House styles: Does both Swedish and English styles. All homes triple glazed.

Services available: design, planning, shell erection.

Address: Bilton Mill Road, West Chiltington, Pulborough, West Sussex, RH20 2PY, 0798 812896.

Factory at: United Downs Industrial Park, St Day, Cornwall TR16 5H, 0209 821805

The Border Design Centre

Reputable Scottish design company with distinctive ranges of houses and considerable expertise in timber frame. Established in 1962 and claimed to be the oldest timber frame company in Scotland, and one of the oldest in the UK. Operates nationwide.

Services available: include design, builder specification, planning and building control application.

Address: Harelaw Moor, Greenlaw, Duns, Berwickshire TD10 6XT, 0578 740218.

Briar Country Homes

Timber frame suppliers specialising in one-off designs. All staff are professionally qualified, and the company offers extremely flexible packages. It will do as much, or as little, as each client wants.

House styles: to customer specification, the company has no standard designs of its own.

Address: St Andrews Works, Charlesfield Road, Horley, Surrey RHG 8BJ, 0293 820100.

Border Oak Design and Construction Ltd

Innovative British company making frames from home-grown oak, using skeletal frame system, not wall panels. The company aims to revive the skills of the Elizabethan carpenters, and its motto is: history in the making.

House styles: oak-framed cottages and farm / manor houses. Some houses have thatch.

Services available: Include self build package with various design options, planning, architectural to complete dwelling.

Address: Kingsland Sawmills, Kingsland, Leominster, Herefordshire HR6 9SF, 0568 708752.

David Boyack Homes Ltd

Scottish manufacturer. Offers any design and also has standard designs of its own. Full build within 100 miles.

Services available: erection, and also full build within 100 miles.

Address: 45 Pottery Street, Kirkcaldy, KYI 3ET, 0592 54757.

Boys and Boden

House styles: to customer specification.

Services available: supply, erection, planning.

Address: British Sawmills, Mill Lane, Welshpool, Powys SY21 7BL, 0938 552051.

Calders Grandridge

This company offers a variety of services of interest to self builders. Their building packs contain all the timber supplies you need to finish a house of either brick and block or timber frame construction on the first floor. The building packs, of roof and floor, first and second fix, are worked out when you send your house drawings, and delivery phased to your building programme. Alternatively, you can simply send in your plans and the company's computer technology will do the whole house. There are also several standard Masterplans, offering virtually unlimited variation.

Address: London Road, Boston, Lincolnshire PE21 7HJ, 0205 366660.

Canadian Cedar Europe

Solid log homes made from imported red cedar. There are 60 standard designs, ranging from a ski chalet to a ranch style 4,000 square foot bungalow, but one-off designs from customers' sketches can also be handled. Packages designed for self builders, and services can be supply only, or supply and erection.

Address: Lodge Cottage, 140 School Lane, Husborne Crawley, Beds, MK43 0UY, 0908 584159.

Cartledge Frames Ltd

House styles: timber frames to customer specification, the company specialises in one-off, high quality packages for self builders, offering supply only or supply and erect.

Address: 507 Weelsby Street, Grimsby, S Humberside DN32 8DW, 0472 358746.

Chatco Timber Structures Ltd

House styles: to customer specification. They specialise in one-off packages for self builders, and have been making timber frames since 1978.

Address: Quarry Lane, Chichester, West Sussex, PO19 2PE, 0243 531818.

Christian Torsten

This company aims to produce timber frame packages comparable with those imported from Scandinavia, but manufactured in North Shropshire to achieve keener prices.

House styles: limitless. Each frame is made individually, to meet Scandinavian levels of energy efficiency. Clients encouraged to come and see frame in production.

Address: Unit B3, Wem Industrial Estate, Soulton Road, Wem, Shropshire SY4 5SD, 0939 233416.

Cheshire Timber Components

Ten year old specialist timber engineering company which offers the Nascor system of wall panelling, used in America for over 70 years, and claimed to be highly cost effective. Nascor provides whole house package, or a structural system only.

Address: Cheshire Timber Components, PO Box 61, Warrington, Cheshire, WA4 4SU.

CMR Construction

NHBC registered house builders and timber frame manufacturers. Offers project management and financial advice. Experienced in design and other services for self builders.

Address: 19 Rossefield, Barrow in Furness, Cumbria LA13 9RF, 0229 811090.

W.H. Colt & Son Ltd

Well known name in timber frame, this company offers a complete range of services for self builders to choose from.

House styles: 65 catalogue styles can be altered to suit customer.

Services available: include drawings, supply of kit and materials, technical advice

Address: Bethersden, near Ashford, Kent TN26 3DE, 0233 820456.

Country Homes

British company with emphasis on personal service. Offers full NHBC cover.

House styles: flexible, from standard range to customer specification.

Services available: supply of kit, erection, planning if necessary.

Address: The Mill House, Marsh Farm, Crosskeys, Withington, Hereford HRI 3NN, 0432 820660.

Custom Homes

Has a book of house plans with more than 200 designs, or will design to customer's specification. Makes the point that any design can be built in timber frame or brick and block but "we are convinced that a timber framed home, clad with brick or stone, offers the best of both worlds – durability, low maintenance and very low heating costs, so low that they are increasingly commanding a premium price on re-sale".

Services available: include full design, planning applications through to build. Help with finance and finding plots.

Address: 45 Station Road, Redhill, Surrey RHI IQH, 0737 768261.

Andrew Davie

Scottish manufacturer.

Address: Eastfield Business Park, Newark Road, South Glenrothes, Fife KY7 4NS, 0592 774444.

Elgin Timber Products

Company with 20 years experience of producing all its timber components.

House styles: timber frame homes to customer specification. Emphasis on quality and flexibility.

Address: 103 Pinefield Industrial Estate, Elgin, Moray IV30 3JF, 0343 549786.

Finwood UK

Log houses, highly insulated and built from pine wood imported from Northern Finland.

House styles: all types of log building. Company works at quality end of market, but

aims to be competitively priced.

Number of models: standard designs but will build to customer specifications. Also does swimming pool enclosures.

Address: Buchanan Works, Strathallan, Auchterarder, Perthshire PH3 IAJ, 0764 64392.

Fleming Buildings Ltd

Scottish manufacturer.

Address: 23 Auchinloch Road, Lenzie, Glasgow G66 5ET, 041 776 1181.

T. Fleming Homes Ltd

Scottish company whose houses have insulation to highest Scandinavian standards.

House styles: one-off designs for customers, and wide range of standards.

Services available: include design, planning applications and Building Regulations, manufacture, delivery.

Address: Station Road, Duns, Berwickshire TDI1 3BR, 0361 83785.

Four Square Design Ltd

Friendly architectural practice with a specific interest in self build. Will design one-offs, or has a range of standards which can be built in brick and block or timber frame. Good reputation for high quality, innovative work.

Address: The Old Surgery, Lambourn, Berks RG16 7NR, 0488 71384.

Frames Homes (South West) Ltd

Established 1974, this experienced company has a reputation for high quality timber frame at extremely sensible prices. Active nationwide.

House styles: bungalows and houses, standard designs and one-offs; the company has a library of over 500 working drawings and a computer aided design facility specifically programmed to help customers incorporate details. Service starts with a detailed site survey, and the company has its own architects. Very flexible

packages offered, from design and supply, to erection and full build.

Address: The Industrial Estate, Station Rd, Perranporth, Cornwall TR6 OLH, 0872 572882.

Fraser Timber Frame Ltd

Scottish company with wide area of activity, manufacturing and designing timber frames.

House styles: to customers' design.

Number of standard designs: 14

Services available: include manufacture to individual customer drawings.

Address: Winterwarm Homes, Drumalbyn Sawmills, Wood Street, Grangemouth FK3 8LH, 0324 483385.

Guardian Homes

This company specialises in individual designs, but also has 50 standard designs of its own, including their particularly innovative Barnholme range where houses look exactly like stone barn conversions. Customers can choose standard and enhanced wall and loft insulation. Competitively priced.

Address: Sowerby Wood Business Park, Park Road, Barrow in Furness, Cumbria, LA14 4QR, 0229 870522.

Guildway Timber Structures Ltd

One of the best known names in British timber frame. In business for over 40 years. Has three distinct ranges of houses, bungalows and chalet-styles, altogether nearly 30 different designs, all adaptable, from the current portfolio plus many earlier designs. Offers a builder service if required.

Address: Frith End Road, Frith End, Bordon, Hants, GU35 0QZ, 0420 488006

Haiku Houses

Fascinating houses of 16th century Japanese design, made with American timbers, using round poles for structural strength. Haiku houses have won several

major awards in the US, all featuring *'great halls'* and *'grand verandas'*. Fabulously inspiring catalogue.

Address: Haiku Houses, American Timber Supplies, Treeve Lane Estate, Hayle, Cornwall TR27 5DQ, 0736 757 594

Hedlunds Swedish Houses

Offers high quality Swedish homes with emphasis on energy conservation and high standards of craftsmanship. Company with a Rolls Royce reputation.

House styles: to customer specification. Clients encouraged to design their own houses, with the help of the company's own design service.

Services available: erection of superstructure, planning and Building Regulations.

Address: Hedlunds House, Beacon Road, Crowborough, Sussex TN6 1AF, 0892 665007.

Herefordshire Timber Frames Ltd

Family run business with nationwide service.

House styles: will work to customer's plans, but also has own portfolio of designs. Services available: build to shell only but will provide custom made joinery; architectural services. Competitive pricing policy.

Address: Bush Bank, nr Dilwyn, Herefordshire, HR4 8EN, 0568 88323

Hertford Solid Log

House styles: single storey and chalet-style houses.

Number of models: 20

Services available: design, supply, erection

Address: 93 Bengeo Street, Hertford, 0992 558529.

Highland Kit Homes Ltd.

Scottish manufacturing company.

Address: 122 Liff Road, Dundee DD2 2TL, 0382 611112.

Malcom T. Holmes

Chartered architect and historic buildings consultant who specialises in designing and commissioning one-off

oak-framed buildings for individual clients; post and beam construction. The houses use early Tudor designs and carpentry techniques; English coppiced oak.

Address: Pelham Lodge, Old Southend Road, Howe Green, Chelmsford, Essex CM2 7TB, 0245 401253.

Roger Hockley

Specialises in quality private house building which combines Scandinavian standards of insulation and energy efficiency with British designs. Offers full build or supply only.

House styles: timber frame to customer specification

Services available: land search with database of 3,000 plots, architectural services; energy management, interior design and landscaping.

Address: 29 Spennymoor Close, North Hykeham, Lincolnshire LN6 9TE, 0522 696348.

Hosby Sale Ltd

House styles: to client specification. Top quality, highly insulated Danish timber frames, with optional extras including saunas, roof development and balconies.

Delivery and assembly: Uses its own specialist three man construction team, house complete within 20 weeks of signing contract.

Services available: planning, building and completion including interiors.

Address: Unit 24, The Nursery, Sutton Courtenay, Oxon OX14 4UA, 0235 848757.

Home Build Services Ltd

House styles: to customer specification; are Guildway agents; friendly, knowledgeable service.

Services available: full project management, land finding, budgeting, planning and design.

Address: 80 Kingshill Road, Dursley, Gloucestershire GLII 4EF, 0453 548211; School House, St Annes Lane, Nantwich, Cheshire CW5 5EH, 0270 610144.

Howarth Timber (Elland) Ltd

Does timber frame packages for self builders, specialising in one-off designs to customer's specification, but also has some standard designs. Nationwide service includes design, supply and erect.
Address: Elland, West Yorkshire, HX5 9DZ, 0422 376012.

IJM Timber Engineering

Irish company with English office for nationwide work, timber frame manufacturers, offering complete design and erection if required, with 300 - 400 standard designs of its own. Delivery time: 6 – 8 weeks.
Address: Commodore House, Switchback Road, Maidenhead, Berks, 0628 773014.

Jackson Campbell Ltd

House styles: timber frame homes to customer specification.
Services available: architectural services; land for sale.
Address: 147 Derby Road, Nottingham NG7 1NE, 0602 242422.

Jones Homes

Welsh company that used to build brick and block, before switching over to timber frame entirely.
House styles: Some standard designs, will build anything to specification. Delivery time: within 4 weeks.
Services available: planning, design, project management, Building Regulations, exterior finish.
Address: Ffordd Las, Llandymog, Denbigh, Clwyd LL16 4LR, 0824 790508

Kildonan Homes Ltd.

Scottish manufacturer.
Address: Unit 6c Bandeath Industrial Estate, Throsk, Stirling FK7 7NP, 0786 815656.

Leisure Lodge

House styles: log chalets.
Delivery time: 2 – 3 weeks.
Assembly time: varies according to model.
Services available: help and advice, site inspection etc.
Address: Horley Lodge Lane, Salfords, Surrey RHI 5EA.

Lindal Cedar Homes

North American timber frame homes from Seattle. Designs based on post and beam construction, with maximum flexibility. Standard designs, and to customer specification. For more than 45 years, has been active in North America, initially Canada, with a huge turnover. Began as a family company, went public in 1971, and now increasingly exports.
Services available: site analysis, feasibility studies.
Address: Designer Homes Partnership, PO Box 3, Bottesford, Nottingham NG13 OEZ, 0949 42551.

Log Home Living Ltd

One and two storey solid log homes imported from Finland. Highly insulated, there are standard designs and the company will also design and build to customer specifications. Supply and erection are always part of the package, or there is a full turnkey service, including interior decor.
Services available: full build, interiors.
Address: Sedge House, North Frodingham, Driffield Y025 8LA, 0262 488418.

Markbohus Ltd

House styles: specialises in one off designs. Sole UK agents for Ekefors timber frame factory in southern Sweden, in business since 1961.
Services available: supply and build. Emphasis on quality and personal service
Address: The Old Barn,

Ancient House Mews, Church St, Woodbridge, Suffolk, IPI 1DH, 0394 383778

Medina Gimson

British company, and a market leader. More than 50 standard designs in several ranges, from 1,000 square feet to 5,000 square feet; their latest Yeoman range is outstanding. Will also design and construct to customer specification. Computer aided design facilities. Option to use energy enhancement package, or their Ecowall system.
Services available: design, planning, Building Regulations, full building if required, but completely flexible packages for self builders.
Address: Medina Gimson Ltd, Bordyke End, East Street, Tonbridge, Kent TN9 1HA, 0732 770992.

Merronbrook Ltd

British firm that has exported timber frames to Scandinavia, which is surely the ultimate in coals-to-Newcastle.
House styles: to customer specification.
Services available: computerised design, planning, others to customer requirement, will do full build if required.
Address: Hazeley Bottom, Hartley Wintney, Hants RG27 8LX, 0252 844747.

T. Mitchell Homes Ltd

Scottish manufacturer.
Address: South End, Thornton, Fife KY1 4ED, 0592 774401.

Moor Park Homes Ltd

Scottish manufacturer.
Address: The Sawmill, Whitelees Road, Lanark ML11, 0555 665087.

Moreys Manufacturing Ltd

Part of a 100 year old timber company that expanded into making and erecting timber frame houses ten years ago. Offers a very flexible system – no standard panel sizes means that each home is individually made to its own design.
House styles: to customer specification, or there is a choice of standard designs.

Nationwide service, competitive pricing.
Services available: full architectural and engineering services.
Address: Portland House, Trafalgar Rd, Newport, IOW P030 1RT, 0983 525111.

Myresjo UK Ltd

British subsidiary of leading timber frame building manufacturer in Sweden. Uses precision built, large panel system, so that the house is usually erected and weathertight in a single day. Average build time, from completed foundations to turning the key, is nine weeks.
Services available: straight kit supply to turnkey contracts Provides on-site advice at all key stages of construction, to help self builders.
Address: 5 Hyde Park Gate, London SW7 5EW 071 584 8737.

Neatwood Homes

British company of 25 years experience in design and manufacture of timber frame. Competitive pricing policy.
House styles: to customer specification.
Services available: supply only or supply and erection. Computer-aided design, programmed deliveries to suit, planning and Building Regulations approval.
Address: Unit 6a Westwood Industrial Estate, Pontrilas, Herefordshire, HR2 OEL, 0981 240860.

Nethan Valley Homes Ltd

Scottish manufacturer.
Address: Turfholm, Lesmahaagow, Lanarkshire ML11 0ED, 0555 894594.

Nordic Homes Ltd

British supplier of Swedish homes, and part of the L.B.Invest Group (Sweden), producing 5000 houses a year, claims to be European leading timber frame manufacturer. Factories in Sweden and Germany.
House styles: various. Using Teknik system, houses normally erected and roofed in a day. Highly energy efficient, NHER energy rating

certificate provided on each house.
Address: Majority House, 51 Lodge Lane, Derby DE1 3HB.

Nordland Homes (UK) Ltd

Swedish company with many years experience. Uses wall units up to 28 feet long complete with glazed windows for rapid erection. Very high insulation (seven inches to walls, ten inches to roof, and three inches to floor, plus triple glazing, insulated doors, and central ventilation system with optional heat-recovery all as standard). House designs are mostly one-offs, but there are standard designs.
Services available: from supply of timber frame through to complete erection. NHBC guarantee. Flexible packages for self builders.
Address: 44-46 Berry Lane, Longridge, Preston, Lancs, PR3 3JJ, 0772 784411.

Norfolk Timber Homes

Cost-effective system.
Address: Church Farm Works, Oulton, Norwich NR11 6NT, 0263 874166.

Oliver Homes

Scottish based, but design, manufacture and supply throughout the UK. Self builders can choose packages, or enlist the services of a professionally qualified area manager to provide a complete service through from planning to completion.
Services available: advice, introduction to local builders to erect packages, planning, financing and construction. More than 120 standard designs in different ranges. Excellent reputation for top of the range homes.
Address: Burnfoot Industrial Estate, Hawick, Scotland TD9 8SL, 0450 73283.

Pacific Wood Ltd

Independent British company distributing cedar homes from America. The system makes for super-quick building, with highly insulated walls finished inside and out – no decoration or plasterboard needed. Houses can be

customised; said to be very warm and durable.
Address: Pacific Wood Limited, The Flour Mill, Wath Road, Elsecar, Barnsley, South Yorkshire, S74 8HW, 0226 747424.

Parkstyle Homes Ltd

This company offers a full range of services for self builders.
House styles: both standard designs and to customer specification. Specialise in colonial styles.
Services available: full project management ie finance, budgets, architectural service, full build and interior design.
Address: PRP Studio, The Paddocks, Stonepit Lane, West Sussex, BN5 9QV, 0273 492445.

Period Homes Partnership

Small British company offering house plans with a difference – roomy American interiors, with traditional British exteriors. This firm is affiliated to an American company EDI, one of the top ten planning and residential practices in the US. Offers a design and build service in both timber frame and masonry.
House styles: approx. 50.
Services available: project management of build (no kit provided) interior design, landscaping, Building Regulations.
Address: 7A Market Street, Crediton, Devon EX17 2EE, 0363 777888.

Pinewood Structures Ltd

Experienced timber frame company with nationwide activities, counts major house builders among its clients as well as individual self builders. It is introducing its own standard designs, but also designs and manufactures to individual customer specification and will offer services as required from design and supply, to full design and build. Very competitively priced.
Address: The Station, Gamlingay, nr. Sandy, Bedfordshire, SG19 3HB, 0767 51218.

Potton Ltd

British firm, high profile market leader, good after-sales service. Impressive show house complex, and free seminars.
House styles: standard designs only, in several ranges, including Heritage cottages, Rectory houses, Shire houses and bungalows. All the designs can be flexible.
Services available: include planning approval and Building Regulations, architectural service in house, site visits from contract managers, supply and erect, garden design service
Address: The Old Foundry, Willow Road, Potton, nr Sandy, Beds, SG19 2PP, 0767 260348

Preference Homes Ltd

Company that provides design, management and construction services on a completely individual basis. Works throughout Kent, Surrey, Sussex, Hampshire, Berkshire, Wiltshire or Oxfordshire. Also handles conversions and brick and block.
Address: Westmead House, 123 Westmead Road, Sutton, Surrey SM1 4JH.

Project Design and Management Ltd

This is a small company which designs, manufactures and erects timber frames, specialising in clients' own designs although it does have some standards of its own. It will design and supply packages, or design, supply and erect. It works within a 150-mile radius of Ipswich.
Address: 1 Days Green, Capel St Mary, Ipswich IP9 2HZ 0473 310537.

Prestoplan Homes Ltd

British company, a market leader, established over 25 years, and active throughout the UK. Each frame made at company's new factory, with computer aided design facility.
House styles: from standard range of 700 designs to customers' own designs.

Services available: You name it, they do it!
Address: Four Oaks Road, Walton Summit Centre, Preston PR5 8AS, 0772 627373.

Purpose Built Ltd

Offers 80 different styles, bungalows to luxury detached houses.
Services available: ready prepared drawings for planning applications at no extra cost, for a very fast start.
Address: Spring Lane South, Malvern Link. Worcestershire WR14 IAQ, 0684 892602.

Robertson Homes Ltd

Well established Scottish company.
House styles: bungalows, 2 storey houses.
Number of standard designs: 20.
Services available: full build depending on area.
Address: Carriden Industrial Estate, Bo'ness, West Lothian EH51 9TA, 0506 822792.

Roy Homes Ltd

Scottish firm specialising in timber frames, standard designs of its own and any one-offs to customer specification. Offers flexible packages to self builders, including kit erection (two days).
Address: 12 Lotland Street. Longman Industrial Estate, Inverness, IVI IPA, 0463 713 838

Scandia-Hus Ltd

Swedish company, well established in Britain, and a market leader. Does both Scandinavian designs and traditional-looking British homes. Superb show house complex in Sussex is well worth visiting. Offers standard designs but customers can adapt. Also designs to customers' requirements. Is making headway with customer care and has introduced a series of free routine visits to check progress of self builders.
Services available: custom designs, planning permission, Building Regulations and after sales service.

Address: Crown Lodge, Canteloupe Road, East Grinstead RH19 3YU, 0342 327977.

Scotframe Timber Engineering Ltd.

Scottish manufacturers.
Address: Inverurie Business Park, Soutarford Avenue, Inverurie AB51 9ZJ, 0467 24440.

Select Timber Frame Ltd

Small family company, emphasis on exceptional customer care and value for money. Active through out Britain.
House styles: unlimited. To customer specification.
Services available: include planning, Building Regulations, erection, working supervision, full build.
Address: Fellgate Works, Hazeley Lea, Basingstoke, Hants, RG27 8ND, 0734 326606.

Skan Norvik Homes

Scandinavian homes imported from Norway, and built in the UK by a Norwegian master builder to each customer's individual order.
House styles: customised; company has its own architectural department.
Delivery time: 6 weeks from signing of contract.
Services available: full build, fitting of kitchens and bathrooms and decoration, kits include standard kitchen.
Address: 9 Hungerford Square, Rosslyn Park, Weybridge KT13 9QS, 0932 852430

Spaceframe Homes Ltd

Small new company set up by property professional who built his own house and patented the system for a 'double' frame. Thick, highly insulated walls and other energy efficient features are intended to make a central heating system redundant.
House styles: unlimited, to customers specification.
Services available: kit supply includes frame, erection, insulation and plasterboard.
Address: Tunnels End,

Harborough Road, Great Oxenden, Market Harborough, LE16 8NA, 0858 432547.

A G Stuart Ltd

Solid log timber houses, not imported but designed in Scotland and made from home grown timber. Active nationwide, with a southern office in Peterborough. Choice of standard designs or to customer specification.
Services available: kit supply or supply and erection.
Address: Old Rayne, By Insch, Aberdeenshire AB5 6RX, 0464 5208.

Taylor Lane Timber Frame

British firm, Herefordshire based, which supplies houses all over UK.
House styles: complete flexibility to accommodate all designs. No standard designs of its own, but will do drawings from any plan submitted by customer. Reckons to offer unbeatable value for money with its packages.
Services available: includes self build advice line; very friendly firm.
Address: Chapel Road, Rotherwas Industrial Estate, Hereford HR2 6LD, 0432 271912.

Roy Thomas Timber Frame

British firm with competitive pricing policy.
House styles: from Tudor-style to ultra modern, built to customer specification (can construct to customer's drawings) Standard range also available.
Services available: supply and erect, or full build service; architectural services and land advice.
Address: Unit 68, Rowfant Business Centre, Rowfant, West Sussex RGH10 4NQ, 0342 718100

The Titus Company

Interesting small company headed by Roger Titus, an American who came to Britain in the late eighties bringing with him 30 years of timber frame experience. Cost effective specialist with

over 600 completed homes on both sides of Atlantic. Has no warehouse, and constructs each frame individually on site, as is the American tradition. Offers free quotation service to customers submitting their own plans. Tries to encourage customers to opt for six inch studwork, as opposed to four, to allow for greater insulation, and says price differential on a 2,000 square ft house is only £400. NHBC registered.
Address: Roger Titus, 34 Gryms Dyke, Prestwood, Great Missenden, Bucks HP16 0LP, 02406 5117.

Torwood Homes (Scotland) Ltd

Manufacturers offering own standard designs and will also manufacture to customer specification.
Address: Royston Road, Deans Industrial Estate, Livingston, West Lothian EH54 8AH, 0506 414104.

Trivsel UK Ltd

Swedish company, offering best of Swedish design and technology with style adaptations for UK market.
House styles: to customer specification or from standard ranges. One off designs provided. Clients can choose between supply only, supply and erection, or full turnkey package. Weathertight shell with prehung windows and doors within 24 hours.
Address: Whinfield House, Whinfield Industrial Estate, Rowlands Gill, Tyne & Wear NE39 IEH, 0207 542935/545955.

Walker Timber Ltd

Timber importers, sawmills and manufacturers, specialising in one-off houses although it has its own standard ranges. Will supply only, or does design and build packages. Uses timber from Sweden, Russia and Canada.
Address: Heatkeeper Homes, Carriden Sawmills, Bo'ness, Scotland, EH51 9SQ, 0506 823331.

Wellgrove Timber Systems Ltd

Scottish manufacturer.
Address: Home Options, Westhill Industrial Estate, Westhill, Aberdeen AB32 6TQ, 0244 742300.

Ystwyth Homes Ltd

Timber frame specialist designing and making to top quality Swedish specification at competitive prices. Number of standard designs: 50 – also build to customer's specifications.
Services available: include supply, erection, planning - as required by customer. Works nationwide.
Address: Llanfarian, Aberystwyth, Dyfed SY23 4NN, 0970 617695.

Other useful sources for self builders of timber frame are:

Association of Self Builders, Hollow End, Hollow Lane, Colton, Rugeley, Staffs, WS15 3LQ. A nationwide association for self builders.

Keith Bishop RIBA, 17 Rayshill Close, Malvern, Worcester WR14 2BP 0684 566494, architect with a specific interest in self build projects, who will provide a nationwide certification service for self builders backed by £250,000 indemnity cover.

Eurisol UK Limited, 30 High Street, Redbourn, Herts AL3 7DL, 0582 794624 (insulation manufacturers association).

Hutchins' Price Schedules Ltd, 33 Station Road, Bexhill-on-Sea, East Sussex, TN40 1RG, 0424 211908 (for annually revised estimating schedules).

Individual House Builders Association (IHBA), 107 Lancaster Gate, London W2 3NQ, 071 262 2218. This body launched in 1992, and aims eventually to be a watchdog for the self build industry.

Juvan Courses, Lower House, Mill Lane, Longhope, Glos GL17 0AA. Runs DIY courses for self builders.

Landbank Services, Elizabeth House, Frances Road, Basingstoke, Hants RG21 3DB, 0256 811774. Nationwide plot - sourcing agency for selfbuilders

Land Registry: 071 405 3488

National Energy Foundation, Rockingham Drive, Linford Wood, Milton Keynes MK14 6EG, 0908 672787. This is a registered charity which administers the National Home Energy Rating Scheme.

National House Building Council, Buildmark House, Chiltern Avenue, Amersham, Bucks HP6 5AP, 0494 434477.

Royal Institute of British Architects, 66 Portland Place, London W1N 4AD, 071 580 5533. Booklets and lists of architects in specific areas who specialise in private housing.

Royal Institution of Chartered Surveyors, 12 Great George Street, Parliament Square, London SW1P 3AD.

SCOFTI (Scottish Consortium of Timber Frame Industries): Stirling Enterprise Park, John Player Building, Players Road, Stirling FK7 7RS, 0786 62122.

Swedish Finnish Timber Council, 17 Exchange Street, Retford, Notts DN22 6BL, 0777 706616.

Swedish House Federation of the United Kingdom, 73 Welbeck Street, London W1M 8AN, 071 935 9601.

Timber and Brick Information Council, Gable House, 40 High Street, Rickmansworth, Herts, WD3 1ES, 0923 778136. Offers help and advice together with useful literature about timber frame.

Timber Research and Development Association, an independent research and development association involved in the development of timber frame construction in the UK since 1962; offers consultancy services, including full architectural design, testing of components, and specialised advice on insulation, ventilation, condensation control, fire and acoustic performance. Regional offices cover UK.
Headquarters: TRADA, Stocking Lane, Hughenden Valley, High Wycombe, Bucks HP14 4ND, 0240 24 3091.
Scotland: Stirling Enterprise Park, John Player Building, Players Road, Stirling FK7 7RS, 0786 62122.

US Softwood Timber Associations, Regent Arcade House, 19-25 Argyll Street, London W1V 1AA, 071 287 2718 (for information about American timber frame products).

Glossary of terms

Aggregate: sand and/or stone mixture, used with cement and sand to make concrete.

Angle grinder: a drill tool with a disc that cuts metal or masonry.

Apron flashing: lead flashing usually placed at the bottom of chimney stacks

Architrave: wooden facing strips around a door or window, which cover the join between the door lining and wall. Architraves are often decorative features in their own right.

Backfilling: where material is first excavated from foundations and then returned to help fill them in.

Barge board: the board which hides and protects the outside edge of the roof of a gable end.

Barge foot: timber piece at the bottom of the barge board, blocking off the gap under the eaves.

Bat: part of a cut brick

Batt: a piece of insulation material, usually mineral wool.

Batten: a piece of timber fixed in place for something to be attached to – notably, rows of battens are put on the roof to hold the tiles.

Bond: the way bricks are laid to overlap, so that they present an attractive appearance and have structural strength.

Breather membrane: waterproof sheeting applied to the outside of a timber frame, to keep water out during construction

Carcass: could be used to describe the frame, including joists and roof timbers.

Cavity: nominally 50mm wide gap in a timber frame, between the external cladding and the timber frame. There to prevent passage of damp.

Cement: powder which forms a paste when mixed with water, then sets hard. Mixed with aggregate and sand to form concrete, and with sand to form screed, mortar or render.

Common brick: a brick of (usually) unattractive appearance, used where it won't be seen – in foundations, for instance.

Compactor: machine with vibrator that compacts material - eg, hardcore in foundations.

Coping: course of bricks on top of a wall.

Corbel: projection of brickwork from a wall, for instance to support a gable, or part of a fireplace.

Course: a course of brickwork is one horizontal layer of bricks. A soldier course is a course laid vertically – for instance, above a window.

Decking: rigid, horizontal sheets of wood laid on to joists as a floor or roof surface.

Dpc and dpm: damp proof course and damp proof membrane respectively. A dpc is a wide strip of plastic laid along the base of the brickwork skin to prevent rising damp. A dpm is plastic sheeting laid under the concrete slab and screed, to prevent damp rising.

Dry lining: when walls are finished with plasterboard rather than plaster.

Eave: the part of the roof that extends beyond the face of the external walls.

Efflorescence: a white deposit that can appear on brick walls, caused by the evaporation of water leaving a deposit of salt. It can be brushed or washed off.

Elevation: the drawing which shows the external appearance of the house.

Engineering brick: a strong clay brick, used where great durability is required.

Facing brick: brick chosen mainly for its aesthetic appearance, to clad external walls.

Fascia: board put over the ends of the roof trusses, to support the gutter.

Felt: laid beneath the tiles, under the battens and over the trusses.

Flashing: lead used to cover external joints, for instance at junctions between windows and chimneys.

Gable end: vertical triangular shape at the end of the house.

Girding rail: a 'belt' which encircles the structure of a post and beam house at first floor level, to hold the upright timbers in place.

Hardcore: broken bricks, rubble and stones, etc., laid as a base underneath concrete – for instance in foundations under the slab.

Heave: where clay ground swells in wet conditions, sometimes due to the removal of trees. Can cause movement in buildings, so where heave occurs, extra care must be taken with foundation design.

Inspection chamber: a manhole placed over the junction of main drains and branches. Inspection chambers are often of pre-formed plastic.

Insulating quilt: term used to describe the insulation inserted in the walls, and in the roof.

Jamb: the inside vertical face of an opening (eg, a door); or the vertical side post of a window or door frame.

Joint: a junction between two elements. For instance, when a dryliner tapes and joints, he is covering up joins in the plaster board.

Jointing: the mortar that is placed between the vertical and horizontal faces of bricks.

Joist: a beam, usually of timber or steel, that supports a decking floor or plasterboard ceiling.

Leaf: a timber frame house has an inner leaf (of timber) and an outer leaf (brick or stone). It is the inner leaf which bears the structural load; the outer leaf is partly there for appearance, partly to protect against weather.

Lintel: a beam placed above doors and windows to take the weight of the wall above, usually of timber in the inner leaf or of steel in the outer leaf of brick or stone.

Mastic: a material used for sealing joints.

Mortise and tenon joint: traditional way of joining two pieces together without nails, and still used. The mortise is the hole, and the tenon fits into it.

Nogging: small piece of timber attached to stud walls before drylining, so that wall-hung items such as radiators, shelves and pictures, can be hung later.

Oversite: concrete base laid over the ground on a hardcore or sand sub-base.

Pointing: the way mortar is raked out between bricks. There are several different styles of pointing.

Profiles: timber boards which mark the foundation boundaries.

Purlin: a beam in traditional roof construction, which supports the rafters. Most modern roofs are of trussed rafter construction.

Raft foundation: a reinforced concrete slab, used for foundations in poor ground conditions.

Screed: smooth sand and cement mixture applied to finish off a concrete oversite floor.

Setting out: marking out on the ground the area where the house is going to be built.

Sheathing board: sheets made of plywood or other wood, nailed to timber studs at calculated points to strengthen the wall panel, making the whole structure stiff and strong.

Skim: thin top coat of plaster, sometimes used on plasterboard to give a slightly more solid feel to the wall. Most plasterboard is, however, finished 'dry' when it is taped and jointed, ready for immediate decoration.

Soakaway: a pit lined with stones which receives surface water off the roof.

Soffit: flat surface beneath the eaves.

Stack: soil pipe running from top of the house down to the drain. Air is sucked into it at the top, and pipes from loos, sinks, etc., run into it.

Studwork: the timber framework of walls.

Taping and jointing: where paper tape is used to hide the joints in plasterboard.

Truss: prefabricated triangular frame for the roof construction.

Vapour barrier: a barrier usually of thick gauge polythene sheeting, but sometimes integral with the plasterboard, which contains moisture produced inside the house. It protects the insulation and stops condensation reaching the timber frame.

Verge: the point at which the brickwork in a gable meets the roof.

ZZZZ: sleep! You've earned it!